What Day Is It?

శుౠ

A Family's Journey
Through
Traumatic Brain Injury

REBEKAH VANDERGRIFF, LMSW

BEAR'S NEST PRESS

KANSAS CITY, MO

2008

)⅃ₑ∾₀ ∂⎫ₑ₎₊ ₋∾•∩ℰ

WHAT DAY IS IT?
A FAMILY'S JOURNEY THROUGH TRAUMATIC BRAIN INJURY.
COPYRIGHT © 2008 BY REBEKAH VANDERGRIFF, LMSW

Layout and Book Design by Chloe Wagner

Front Cover photo: Practice head shot taken while working for Montage Talent Agency, Dallas, TX. Never used by photographer for commercial purposes.

Back Cover photo by Sharon Eiker

Excerpt from *A User's Guide to the Brain: Perception, Attention, and the Four Theaters of the Brain.* by John J. Ratey
Copyright © 2001 by John J. Ratey, M.D.
Published by Pantheon Books, a division of Random House, Inc.
Reprinted by arrangement with the author.

Bear's Nest Press, Box 84, Independence, MO 64051
Telephone: (816) 252-1176; Fax: (816) 252-1176
www.BearsNestPress.com

Library of Congress Cataloging-in-Publication Data

Vandergriff, Rebekah E.
    What day is it : a family's journey through traumatic brain injury /
Rebekah E. Vandergriff.
       p. ; cm.
    Includes bibliographical references.
    ISBN 978-0-9820522-0-4
       1. Brain damage--Patients--Biography. 2. Brain damage--Patients--Family relationships--Biography. 3. Brain damage--Patients--Rehabilitation. 4. Head--Wounds and injuries--Patients--Biography.
       I. Vandergriff, Rebekah E.   II. Title.
    RC387.5 V67   2008

16 15 14 13 12 11 10 09 08   1 2 3 4 5

It is a waste of time to be angry about my disability. One has to get on with life and I haven't done badly. People won't have time for you if you are always angry or complaining.

Stephen Hawking (1942 -)

Somebody has to do something, and it's just incredibly pathetic that it has to be us.

Jerry Garcia (1942-1995)

TABLE OF CONTENTS

Acknowlegements

This has been quite an experience attempting to recall and to learn about what was happening to my body while I wasn't there. I want to thank my family and friends who gave me the material to work with through their responses to my questionnaire and their conversations that jogged my memory. Without their contributions of memories, this book would not have been possible.

Thanks to my many readers at all stages of my book's development. I began by harassing family members, such as, Joe Vandergriff II, PhD. *(I hope I didn't overwhelm your already busy schedule.)* Many family members would avoid me in angst when I would ask for a read-through.

I admit I used a few chapters as learning tools disguised as proofreading, by taking advantage of the students performing their internships and various duties at communityworks, inc. (cwi). Thanks also to online acquaintances, especially Nadine Laman, (author of the *Kathryn's Beach* trilogy) who so graciously offered me software, gave me confidence, and warned me of the tricks of the publishing trade.

Thanks, of course, to Dr. Janet Williams, and everyone involved at cwi who gave me an array of insights. To all the people involved in this slow process—you know who you are—thank you. It's so easy for me to forget names, please forgive me if I've left anyone out.

Cwi was the perfect situation for me. (Thanks to my husband Jeff for finding cwi in the want ads.) The CEO of Communityworks, Dr. Janet Williams, agreed to be my supervisor for my internship, which was required to complete my MSW program at the University of Kansas. She included me as a speaker about recovery from TBI at several conferences that took place between 1998 and 2003. She made opportunities available to me that have allowed me to obtain much-needed confidence. As a person with "relearned ability," it was exactly what I needed after such a crushing blow to my self-esteem.

Many thanks to my editors—I will forever remember the way Linda Rodriguez and Chloe Wagner openly shared their expertise and knowledge that have made such a difference in the quality of this work. In the beginning, Linda Rodriguez did wonders for the organization and structure of this book. Then, Chloe Wagner worked wonders as she fine-tuned the book line-by-line. We often bantered words back and forth as she coached me to get at the exact meaning I intended. Most of all, thank you, Chloe, for believing in me, and telling me that my writing was a "diamond in the rough."

Thanks to the doctors M. Jones, C. Kelly, and Y. Crabtree (and her nurse Camille), plus all of the many people related to their support systems, I now have the use of many tools, which continue to help me cope from day-to-day.

Most of all, I want to express how important my family has been throughout my recovery, and throughout the process of giving birth to *What Day Is It?* My daughters Gabby, Camille, and Olivia, and my husband Jeff are most important in my life today. Special thanks to my mom, Sharon Eiker, who never left my bedside in the hospital, and who was so instrumental in helping me heal, knowing just when it was safe to let go. And thanks to my dad, Sam Dyer, Sr., for contributing the money to print the first run of books.

The year of 1989 was a time when I was in need of so much guidance to understand everything. Thankfully, with everyone's help, I no longer feel as if I am in a bad dream, wondering, "*What Day Is It?*".

Editor's Note

When I first met Rebekah Vandergriff in 1989, she was lying in a hospital bed in a coma. I never imagined then that she would *not only survive* but earn her AA, BA, and MA degrees, get married, have three wonderful daughters, and nearly 20 years later I would be the editor and publisher for her first book!

This is my first book, too—as a publisher—and I am thankful to Rebekah for giving me the opportunity to share my talents. It has been a learning process for both of us as we worked together on this book, and for me, a chance to put to use all of my education in English, publishing, and prepress. A special thanks to my mother, Constance Wagner, for providing financial support during this endeavor.

Rebekah and her mother Sharon are remarkable people. I am blown away when I think of all Rebekah's accomplishments post-injury. I was, and still am, impressed at how Sharon never left her daughter's side—forcing herself to stay awake for nearly two weeks—and with the gutsy way she took charge of her daughter's treatment options. When I visited, I got to hear some of the stories in this book right after they happened. Years later, when my car narrowly missed going over the edge of an icy exit ramp, all I could think of was Rebekah.

Chloe Wagner
Bear's Nest Press, 2008

What Day Is It?

~Chapter One~

When the World Stopped

June 3, 1989

Mother's reaction:

Rebekah was dead on the scene when the Fire Department arrived and resuscitated her. She had pulled her CRX, a small car, onto a two-way busy street from a stop sign and into the path of a speeding car. Rebekah's car was thrown one hundred and thirty feet. A light pole stopped the flight. The bolts sheared off under the seat, and she was thrown about the car, hitting her head on the metal door frame and the steering wheel. In a flash second Rebekah's life was changed forever.

I never pass that Fire Department without a feeling of gratitude. A couple of minutes one way or the other is the difference between life and death. The city billed us for the light pole. We paid the bill but fifteen years later it still leans to remind me as I pass, this is the place where Rebekah had her accident. At the hospital in the emergency room, Rebekah was barely recognizable. Her hair was caked with dried blood. She was on a ventilator for breathing, and the nurse told me she was in a coma. Her head was so swollen I couldn't see her eyes. She had broken clavicles and tubes everywhere. I felt like I had come to visit someone who wasn't home.

I sat by her bed all night telling her we would keep her body warm if she wanted to come back. Tucking her in, smoothing her sheets looking for things to make her comfortable, and to keep my-self busy. It was surreal. The ting ping taps and hum of machines in the emergency room made it all seem sort of inhuman.

The human brain, suspended in fluid encased in the skull, has limited room to move side-to-side or up-and-down. It seems to be magically levitating on top of the spinal column, only connected by a thin cord, in this highly evolved mammalian system.

The night of my accident, a casual neglect to fasten my seat belt sent my brain on a crash course only four blocks from the site where I had entered my car. The impact as I was hurled forcefully about the car threw my brain haphazardly in every direction. The subsequent decision by a doctor, not to place a cut in the back of my skull to allow swelling, left my brain with little room to expand and relieve its building pressure. This, coupled with a lack of oxygen at the scene, vast cerebral inflammation, seizures, and scarring caused damage to my brain that will take a lifetime to repair.

A person may have an open or a closed brain injury. An open brain injury results from penetration or breaking of the skull. In addition, the brain can be traumatized through a blast injury. This occurs from being in close proximity to an explosion and may cause the brain to experience diffuse damage. The brain injury experienced is dependent on location of the explosion, protective gear worn (like in the military), and how close the person is to the blast. Brain injuries may or may not be followed with a period of unconsciousness. A closed brain injury may be the result of a car accident or a blow to the head. Mine was a closed brain injury. A brain injury, open or closed, is labeled traumatic when extensive swelling results in a comatose state.

The damaged brain can be compared to a broken leg that is put in a plaster cast to heal. Both heal slowly with pain and discomfort. But unlike with a broken leg, others do not see the signs of a broken brain. Minus recognizable signs such as crutches, brain injury can even be mistaken for intoxication and treated with scorn.

The brain also heals with a different kind of pain and discomfort than the leg. The pain may be confusion, frustration, anger, or unexpected inappropriate behavior in public or in private; these are all visible symptoms of the invisible trauma but are not recognized by the untrained eye. As a result the discomfort during the healing process is often not even caused by the injury, but by the public's reactions as the survivor is forced to deal with rude comments and glares. It is much easier to accept when the observer can recognize outward signs of the problem.

Trained professionals, family members, or true friends who are willing to slow down and listen to the slow processing of speech *and to allow the extra time for the injured person to express her thoughts* are necessary components of recovery. The general public does not have the patience—if money is not being exchanged—to wait for a stranger moving in slow motion with a speech impediment to express her ideas or needs.

While engaged in conversation, the survivor may have difficulty focusing, and may become fatigued from all the mental activity. It takes concentration to tune out all the extraneous noises, voices, and choices. It takes focus and time to find the right words to express the ideas or needs. People do not realize this broken social response is simply part of the healing, as compared to a broken leg in a cast that is so easily recognized and accepted.

An inappropriate course of action coming from the broken brain is assumed to be a "problem behavior," or "acting out," both of which have negative connotations. There are few who realize that the person behind all the confusion is struggling silently, in his own head to grasp for the word that could easily communicate his thought. There is no visible clue to supply a logical reason for the actions demonstrated by the Traumatic Brain Injury (TBI) survivor.

The unspoken physical or mental reaction may not be overtly expressed, but it's obvious to the survivor who finds herself traveling down this road. A new route has been directed, with many unexpected twists and turns, and this route encompasses her entire new existence. No one willingly decides to travel down this road of transformation, change, and "different ability." The destination is acceptance of their new existence. Not a popular vacation spot. Because this injury is not explainable from the outside, many avoid, deny, or distract themselves from having to confront their new reality.

This is why TBI is referred to by some as the silent epidemic, the hidden injury, the unspoken or invisible wound. The brain is never the same as before the injury, but it *is* elastic and in time may reroute the information pathways, albeit processing at a slower pace than before. It keeps perfecting itself through repetition. The swollen brain within the skull has an incredible capacity to heal through patience and hard work. As the signals repeatedly run into the scarring and make new connections, the information requested is retrieved and put into action to form a thought.

This is the story of my personal journey of recovery from TBI, a story of recovering from a near-death experience and of living life with a disabling closed-brain injury. I want to enlighten readers about the awesome power their brain has to heal. My hope is that people working with brain-injured individuals, or perhaps a person who has encountered his own tragedy, can learn from my experiences and mistakes.

My previous existence was drastically altered when I was found dead at the scene of the accident. Emergency medical workers, with their quick response, gave my life back to me. My mistake, not clicking my seat belt, abruptly ended life as I knew it. I was forced to accept a different life and a different state of mind in an altered body with a declined socioeconomic status. It wasn't my choice to have an accident, but it is my choice what I do with the results of it.

I have come to realize that this very unfortunate injury has become the most liberating event of my life—liberating me to grow and allowing my life to take a completely different direction. It was as if I now was given the chance to choose the other fork in the road. Damage to my brain, which will affect me for the remainder of my life, has become a gift.

Had this event never happened, I would not have had the opportunity to become so free—free to explore who Becky was, and through my internal changes, to explore who Rebekah is to become. I was set free from the chains of what other people thought of me or expected from me. Free, to let go of what Mary Pipher describes in her book, *Reviving Ophelia*, as "the imaginary audience syndrome."

I am able to give up my egocentric self that tried so hard to impress everyone else, so I could "take a bow" for my imaginary audience.

Fifteen years post-injury, my mother and I decided to write down our memories. We read our short essays to each other each week at a local coffee shop. This book is my attempt to explain my perspective on the long journey of learning to function in everyday life with the results of my injuries.

I didn't even know what the words "brain injury" meant when I was told my diagnosis in the hospital. Toward the end of my "summer vacation," I was finally able to understand what had happened and where I had been for the entire summer.

My journey would be incomplete without including the reactions from loved ones, their first visits, and the discovery of my sustained injuries. Finally, this is the story of the death of a materialistic, superficial but fun-to-be-with Becky Dyer, and the birth of a loving mother and fun-to-be-with educated wife, Rebekah Vandergriff, LMSW.

~Chapter Two~

Family Gathers 'Round

The next day Sam, Rebekah's father, arrived. He hit her on the chest and called out, "Becky, Becky, wake up!" Sam had a hard time dealing with what he couldn't see. Things like, as we sat with Rebekah, her brain was swelling—more and more damage was taking place right in front of us, but we couldn't see it.[1]

Later that day, a neurological surgeon came by, and the first thing he did was hit Rebekah on the chest and call out, "Rebekah wake up, wake up." I said, "I'm not sure what they are paying you to do that but we got a crop-duster (her father) that can do that." We all had a good laugh out of it.

You might say, "How could you laugh at a time like that?" I say, "How can you not laugh at a time like that?" Humor became very important over the next few months. It was part of our survival tactics and Rebekah's recovery. Humor was the thin thread of sanity we hung onto to keep from sinking into despair.

When I began the slow process of writing this book, I made up a questionnaire and sent it to family and friends asking for

---

1 The memories of my mother, Sharon Ann Eiker, are set apart in a different type style throughout the book. Her perspective on my progress has been valuable. Mom is an extraordinary writer and a poet, and has kept a personal journal for years, even before the accident. One day she said to me "I wonder if anyone else will read these personal journals, someday when I'm gone." I wondered silently," Why? No one else could decipher the codes of her unique penmanship." I am happy to be able to share some of it through this book.

help filling the blanks in my recollections. (You can read this questionnaire for yourself in appendix 3.) Their stories, feelings, and memories were invaluable as I went through the process of understanding where I had been and how I had grown.

My brother Sam responded this way:

"I was living in Knoxville, Tennessee when I heard the news on June 3, 1989. I drove all night to see Rebekah in ICU. Ten of our family gathered in prayer all night long.

"At last, I was admitted to the ICU to see Becky, road-weary and tearful. Becky's breathing tube was blocked by fluid. I alerted the nurse who then drained it. I was dressed in a suit, and no less than three doctors babbled at me about her. I felt Becky's left foot; it felt normal. I felt her right; it was cold.

"Becky was on a ventilator, but she looked strong. I prayed with the nurses. I held Becky's hand, her right cold hand. We all prayed, and step-brother John Makings said, 'That is the most perfect prayer I have ever heard.' All were crying and weeping—the doctors were so negative."

My sister Nancy remembers the first days like this:

"It was around two o'clock in the morning that I got a phone call from Becky's friend Beth. Beth told me that Becky had been in an accident and that she was in the CAT scan being examined for injuries. I was stunned, and so was my husband, Jeff. We got in the car and drove to Mom's house to tell her. At the time, Mom didn't have her phone hooked up. It didn't take her long to get down the stairs to open the door, and we all went to the hospital. I felt I didn't have any emotions at all. I was in shock and the hospital staff wouldn't let us look at her until four or five hours later.

"She was in intensive care when we did get to see her. Becky had a very bruised jaw, and her clavicle bones were protruding like broken bird wings. She looked like a bird that fell out of a nest. Her wings were broken, and she was teetering on the edge of death. If she weren't being fed oxygen through the accordion medical-breathing devices, she would not be alive, from what the medical personnel told us. The ICU care staff had her attached to a respirator, and it was doing the breathing work.

"My first question was how long she would be hooked up to the breathing machine. They responded, 'She will be on it until she can breathe on her own.'

"I remember cringing at the sight of her lying there helpless. I went over to Becky and said, 'We all love you and you'll be all right.' I don't think she could hear me, but I wanted to tell her that. Somehow, I knew that she would pull through.

"She looked really swollen in the facial area and there wasn't much hope being expressed by the staff. Mom said, 'The doctors are being very grim about the possibility that there is swelling of the brain.' This was really frightening because for that type of thing, doctors have to drill holes in the skull to drain excess fluid that is causing the swelling. They thought the swelling was isolated along the brain stem, and they didn't have to do such invasive measures in this case.

"Except for Mom, none of us were allowed to be in the ICU for very long, and it was best that we weren't because it was too heavy for most of us to look at Becky like this. She was all bloody and mangled and looked like she had been to hell and back. The only thing we could do was to be patient, and pray, pray, pray. A lot of people came to see Becky. She was very popular. Even old boyfriends showed up to pay their respects. Everyone wanted her to pull through this horrible trauma she was suffering."

My sister Debbie remembers those times this way:

"I got the phone call in the middle of the night. 'Becky was in a car accident. Hurry up and get to the emergency room at the hospital.' I don't remember who it was that called me. I think it may have been our sister Nancy. My husband (boy-friend at the time), Eric, drove me to the hospital.

"Someone said, 'Becky may not make it.' I lost it. I started wailing and fell to my knees. When I first saw her in the Neurological Intensive Care Unit, she looked like a monster. Her head was swollen and she was unrecognizable. I cried every day she was in the hospital. I felt such a loss.

"Our father came up to see her. All Becky's past loves came to visit her. We joked that we should have put a revolving door on her room for all of her boyfriends. The doctor took the family out in the hallway and told us that she would probably never wake up, that she was in a coma, and if she did wake up she would never walk or talk again."

Mother's partner, Carl, has different memories of those days:

"I didn't know Rebekah well before her car accident. I knew her only as Sharon's daughter, but I had a sense of a young woman burning through her life at a desperate speed. After the crash, Rebekah was in a coma. The doctors said she probably wouldn't recover. Luckily, Sharon refused to give up hope. We kept Rebekah stimulated through talk and touch, and eventually she began to wake up.

"The first stir of life was in her leg, which she bent and stretched as though stepping on a brake pedal, over and over and over. She came back into the world slowly, groping towards a bit more consciousness every day. It seemed as though she was in a half-dreaming state for weeks. For some time she couldn't speak."

Even the people I went to high school with in Marshall, Missouri heard about my accident and my condition. My friend Katy remembers hearing of the accident this way:

"In January of 1981, Becky came from the city and lived with her dad in our small town to attend school. Becky became part of the 'in crowd' of older students in high school and spent a lot of time with them, as well as dating older guys. The last I had heard of Becky after high school was that she became a model in Dallas. Her friends back home heard stories of her exciting life and high-powered acquaintances. The next story we heard was of her being involved in a serious car accident in 1989, where she sustained injuries from which she was unlikely to recover. Speculation was made as to whether or not Becky would be able to walk or talk again.

"Someone said her father had gone into her hospital room, took one look at her badly broken body and face, yelled out "Becky!" and left the room. Nobody knew exactly what to expect. But we knew that she was in an extensive coma. News of Becky's recuperation then came mainly from hearsay, some of which was said to have come from her family. I had heard her long road to recovery, beginning at an outpatient rehabilitation center and continuing therapy at her mother's home."

Katy Wolfe (right) talks with my stepmom, Mary Dyer (left).

Having lived the majority of my life after experiencing a TBI, I fully believe that, if given the opportunity, many TBI survivors would surprise their family members or care-givers with the progress that can be achieved when the injured individual is given the chance to make decisions—whether they are right, wrong, or foolish—allowed the chance to personally feel the consequences of their behaviors or decisions, made to be independently responsible for experiencing life, not sheltered, coddled, or constantly excused from inappropriate social behavior but brought back into reality. With an outpatient program in which they are consistently presented with ideas for individualized rehabilitation goals and given positive feedback that is personally earned, the resulting progress could amaze the professionals that get paid a salary for doing what Mom did instinctively.

Fortunately, my mother was not forced financially to work a full-time job and was able to attend to my needs each and every moment throughout my hospital stay. She was then able to do the most difficult but necessary work of following my lead about when to back off to allow my own progress.

Mom has a plethora of wise and comical moments she recalls to help me understand what was happening to my body throughout my hospitalization:

The doctor had told her father and sister Debbie that she was not going to make it. This is why they didn't set the collarbones or worry about opening the skull to let the brain have room to swell without further brain damage. I refused to hear that she was not going to make it. An ambulance driver, who was a friend of mine, shared that he visits the Recovery Unit as a follow-up on some people he had left in the Emergency Room. He said, "People die here from secondary injuries. If you have family here, stay with them." Therefore, I stayed with Rebekah until she left the hospital.

I would never recommend parents defy their doctors, but I will say there is no greater force on Earth than a mother's instinct for the survival of her child. It may not be documented in the medical journals, but it is true nevertheless. Trust yourself: be involved, be proactive, do not let all the white coats intimidate, be confident about your familiarity with your child, and realize you know more than you think you know. When everything in you says they are wrong, speak up, get a second opinion and take action.

Rebekah's bottom front tooth had been knocked out in the wreck. She was still in a coma weeks after she left the emergency room. Her teeth were clenched shut tight, and the tube through her nose was her only source of nourishment. A tooth broken out seems unfortunate until you hear the whole story.

The doctors told me, "Rebekah's automatic swallow reflex is not functioning." Instead of swallowing, she drooled. I was asked to sign a paper giving permission for the surgery to put a tube in her stomach. I had reservations about this surgery for several reasons. A nurse had told me it was her experience that patients who were trying to pull out their tubes were ready to eat.

Rebekah was cuffed and tied down when I was asleep or out of the room. Even though she was in a coma, she was cunning. She took any opportunity to roll out of bed or tear at her tubes. I swathed out Rebekah's mouth every day several times with cotton swathes dipped in lemon juice. I worked the swath between her clinched teeth through the space of the missing tooth. In this manner I moistened her tongue which was dry. On a couple of occasions, I saw what appeared to be a swallowing motion in her throat. This swallowing movement made me question the surgery.

The next morning, a nurse placed a sign on Rebekah's bed: No Food, Surgery Today. My instincts told me that anesthesia could not be good for a person we're trying to wake up and that putting her further out of consciousness could be irreversible. In making my decision, I remembered a news story about a family whose daughter had been on life support for seven years. The signature that allows the tubes to be put in will not legally allow them to be removed. When Rebekah left the emergency room and went to the first floor, the doctors told me that she would be vegetative and I should pick out a state hospital. The thought of my beautiful daughter tied to a bed with tubes in her was more than I dared imagine. The daughter on TV was bloated, pasty-faced, and staring at the ceiling, as her family sat around her stuck in time, unable to go on with their lives.

I immediately sent Sarah, my ten-year-old, down to the cafeteria for a chocolate shake. I decided to take the chance and offer Rebekah something to eat. I worked the straw though the small gap from her missing tooth, and she began to suck. It struck me like when she first nursed from the breast when she was born. "She will be strong and thrive," I said to myself. When they came to take her to surgery, I exclaimed with confidence, "she has eaten."

The room filled with white coats. I was told, "She will need a swallow test. If she doesn't pass, she will be rescheduled." Rebekah was constantly on display for the student doctors at this teaching hospital, and the disappointment was felt when all had lined up to watch surgery and all they got was a swallow test.

The swallow test consisted of Rebekah in a sitting position with a fluoroscope revealing the journey of a cube of gelatin from her mouth to her stomach. I was thrilled as I watched the cubes progress. Then they pried open her mouth and placed a dry cracker on her tongue. I held my breath for fear Rebekah would choke on a dry cracker. I saw her tongue lift, and the cracker also traveled down the esophagus. Yeah! She could swallow.

Back in the room, the doctor reported the results of the test to me. Surrounded by white coats, I was informed in no uncertain terms, "Rebekah will need to consume 2400 calories a day or surgery will be rescheduled, and her food consumption will be monitored every day."

I had never witnessed Rebekah consume 2400 calories in one day, and furthermore her jaw was clenched shut. This was a challenge.

I daily ordered the food from the menu, fulfilling the requirement, and I confess Sarah and I ate her food for her. I sent my partner, Carl, to the health food store to buy yogurt, honey, eggs, wheat germ, bananas, and applesauce. He also brought a blender from home. I mixed this concoction twice a day, and she had chocolate malt in the evening. This went on until her jaws relaxed, then she ate oatmeal with honey, smashed bananas, and brown sugar, plus other foods that were readily hand fed until she could feed herself. Each little victory was celebrated by all.

Rebekah is close to 5'11" tall and weighed 114 pounds. Skinny as a beanpole, she slowly rose and stood behind her wheelchair. Then laboriously, she pushed it through the threshold of the hospital door to continue her journey home, and not to a state hospital. After her successful transfer from the wheelchair to the car she said, "I promised my dad I would walk out of there! Now, where's the seat belt?"

Carl and Sharon chat.

Becky (16) and Sarah (4)

~CHAPTER THREE~

Realizing the Losses

All the different nurses, doctors, attendants, this is all so mind boggling to even attempt to recall for Becky. I am pleased that we have grown to the point that we can help Becky make sense of it all, and we can all heal as a family through her compilation of memories. Everything passed by us so fast as we traveled through the hospital dependent on Becky's recovery. First we went to Emergency, to intensive care, recovery, then to the hospital ward floor for rehabilitation. This is where our family encountered Dr. Kelly. He was the first doctor that was honest with me and reported to me that science just doesn't know how much of Becky will recover, be the same, or never communicate again. He said to me that this is where the mother instinct picks up and knows more than science. These words made me feel as if he was giving me permission to speak my opinion and take charge, not giving up hope but keep expecting more of Becky to appear.

The room we were assigned on this ward barely had a touch of green outside the window but plenty of blue sky for our gaze. The first sign I experienced Rebekah voicing was when we were lying down on her hospital bed, now on the floor (as I demanded), we had our feet up on the wall, looking out of the window after watching a program with Joseph Campbell that explained the use of vocal cord sounds using the meditation mantra "oh ah um," all as separate sounds. As I was demonstrating the sound, Becky reached over to my chest and felt the reverberation that the sound vibrated then vocalized through my mouth.

Becky then placed her same hand on her chest and said ah. I was so excited, I continued repeating the sounds as if the room was filled with stones and monks in brown robes. Using my mother's instinct, like Dr. Kelly suggested, Becky found her voice box through the meditation humm of "oh ah um."

When I hear these stories about me, I am amazed that there still exists a person who would be able to live a rich and fulfilling life, accepting the challenges that come after this type of trauma to the brain. Perhaps this is disbelief most medical staff experience while treating a TBI survivor; therefore, they think all people who have experienced a brain injury must be unable to understand what they are saying.

Before my trauma if I were asked, "Would you like to be kept alive through life support systems?" I think that the Becky who existed then would have said, "Don't keep me alive if I am unable to control my own destiny." And that would have been the end to my life; I never would have experienced all the richness of life I have enjoyed since I left behind that young, egocentric twenty-two year-old women.

At the time of our death-defying collision, I would not have chosen to live at my mother's house. I would not have chosen to live at my father's house. I don't know where I would have gone. Adults who have no family alive would go to a nursing home. What if a nursing home had been my first destination point? One's destiny is dependent on the support systems in place at the time of need. My life could have gone many different directions. I am just glad that it has transpired in the manner that it has. Growing up all over again is not an easy thing to do.

"Do you give credit to God?" I am frequently asked. There are many people who would like me to give the short, expected answer, "Yes." But instead, as I have characteristically done since my TBI, I respond with the not-asked-for, longer, thought-provoking explanation.

"There is a power that kept me alive," I say, "Should I name this strength God? If that is what a person is content and familiar with, I don't see why not. But, in my brief encounter with death, the preconceived notion of the Golden Gates is not my experience. I just recall an unexplained darkness."

Could I have visited Hell because of this darkness I recall? If that is how the individual has to delineate the complex nature of our existence, then yes. I just know that I never want to go there again. That non-feeling, emotionless blankness was evident in my expression. My mother knew when my inherent strength came alive in my once lifeless body. The twinkle in my eye returned. The familiar look that only a mother or a loved one has the ability to recognize. I give credit to that inner strength, which was obvious throughout my struggling and remains with me today.

Looking back at my coma days, Mother recalls a change in my hand-eye coordination much earlier than my brain began to heal enough for me to recall any memories.

One day in the Recovery Unit in the hospital, Rebekah opened her eyes. I lifted her bed to a sitting position and put a tray in front of her. I placed a pencil in her left (non-dominant) hand and asked her to write her name. She printed BECKY. That night she had what looked like a seizure. I told the nurses and they said it wasn't anything to worry about. The next day, Rebekah couldn't write her name.

I have a theory that when the nurses see "Constant Vegetative State" written on a chart, they tend to ignore the patient and focus on those they feel they can help. The medical staff believed she would never wake up. I'm sure they thought, "Her poor ignorant mother. She must be in denial." Maybe that's too harsh. Oh well, it was an honest emotion I felt at the time.

When her sisters were in the room, we would include Rebekah in the conversation, even though she was still unconscious. I would get in bed, sit behind Rebekah, and we would clap and sing. It was better than seeing her limp and lifeless. I'm sure it looked pretty crazy on the monitors and perhaps it was a little crazy. So be it!

My sister Nancy recalls a time in this same hospital unit when she was confronted by the nursing staff for her unusual tactics of trying anything to get a reaction from my blankness. Apparently, the nursing staff *did* watch the monitors at times!

"After the second week, I wanted to stimulate your sense of smell," Nancy writes. "I wrapped some herbs from my garden in aluminum foil and brought them in for you. I brought the foil up to your nose. You responded strongly to the lavender, but I didn't get much of a chance to crush more of the herbs for you. At this time, the nurse was monitoring the camera above your bed and caught me in the act of trying to give you aromatherapy. Evidently, this nurse thought it was suspicious behavior."

Nancy was instrumental in my recovery, as were other family members on different occasions. Everyone was having to redefine their roles during this time, and it wasn't always easy. Even my ten-year-old sister and eight-year-old nephew were involved in the struggle when they tried to help and were dealt with harshly.

As Nancy remembers, "We couldn't leave you for a second, but at least your bed was on the floor, thanks to Mom. One afternoon, Mom and I went out in the hall to discuss plans regarding moving your things out of your apartment which you had inhabited just prior to your accident. We left Sarah and Jeffrey in the room alone with you.

"After about five minutes, we heard a crash. Sarah was trying to help you to the bathroom, and at the time, she was about half your size. Mom and I jumped all over Sarah and Jeffery, but it wasn't really their fault. We just became more aware of how quickly you could get hurt. After that point, it was painfully apparent that an adult should always be present in your room. Mom made sure of this until your release from the hospital.

"My now twenty-one year old son, Jeffrey, still remembers this incident and feels guilty for not catching you when you fell. Sarah knew she had been unduly punished and didn't volunteer to do any more 'Becky-sitting' by herself. Still, she was always a good attendant during your recovery. Probably because you were such a wonderful sister to her, and she maybe felt grateful that you were alive. You wore a big bruise from that fall."

Sister Debbie sent me the following memory of this time:

"After ten days, she opened her eyes. She was still alive! I was very confused when she opened her eyes. She wasn't really there. It was like she was empty, a newborn looking around blankly, not focusing. She wasn't 'awake' yet.

"My mom stayed at the hospital every night. She doesn't trust hospitals or doctors. Becky would writhe and flail around on the bed involuntarily. She had a big, gaping wound on her stomach where they checked to see if she had any internal bleeding. It was a nasty looking wound. They had a catheter in her too, and sometimes there would be blood in her urine. Her clavicles were broken from the impact of the wreck. They never set them because they didn't think she'd live. That's probably why they didn't care about the big, oozing hole in her stomach. Mom was smart to stay with her. Becky was moving around a lot and it was getting dangerous."

In the movies a person "awakes" out of a coma, and regains full consciousness within thirty seconds. In reality, depending on the damage and the area of the brain, it may take weeks, months, or even years. There are many stages of becoming aware. The Glasgow Coma Scale is a tool the medical staff uses to rate a patient's progression. One of the stimuli first recognized is the pain stimulus.

Mom told me of a time when the tape was stuck to my skin from the diaper placed to catch my accidents. Here I was, the lights were on but nobody was home, and I can remember when they pulled my skin off with the tape. I was twenty-two and in a diaper, what a humbling past existence! That was probably my first memory.

I didn't believe anyone when they told me I was in the hospital. My mom told me that one evening after an intense display of anger and disbelief, she had to wheel me all the way outside to read the sign in front of the hospital, pointing to each word as she read it, before I would settle down. I don't remember reading the sign, but I do remember being constantly told by my therapists that I was in the hospital. I never believed them until Mom showed me the sign.

When I was becoming potty-trained again at twenty-two, I was still unable to walk. Mom began carrying me to the bathroom. By reading my physical signs, she knew just when it would be time for me to relieve myself. I then learned how to shake my left foot to clue others in at my time of need. Mom must have been out of the room at one of these times when my sister Nancy and brother-in-law Jeff were visiting. Nancy tells about giving me a toy that squeaked when it was squeezed. I squeaked that toy constantly for days until my family had had enough. On this particular day, for some reason, Jeff was elected to carry me to the bathroom following my sign at my time of need. I remember thinking, *What is he doing standing in the bathroom next to me? This is my sister's husband.* Somehow, I communicated to him that he should leave. Thinking that I had no injuries, I tried to stand up and leave once I was finished. Down I went. That woke me up: I realized that I couldn't walk.

There were many times when I thought I could just stand up and walk. Mama Bear (a nickname the nursing staff awarded my mother) insisted my bed was put on the floor to prevent falls. After a series of painful events and repeated falls, I must have started to realize my existence. No one knew that while I endured these painful experiences, I was slowly forming connections in my damaged brain to build my awareness.

One night I will never forget: I was lying awake on the bed; Mom and Sarah were asleep, and it was quiet on this ward of the hospital. The phone was down on the floor next to me in my bed. I remembered the phone number for the bank's Time and Temperature line, 844-1212, and even remembered to add the number 9 to dial out from a business. With my double vision, I located the correct sequence of numbers, and I dialed the number! The pre-recorded message recited its usual mumbo jumbo the bank has plugged in to make you listen, in an effort to keep your attention before revealing the listener's actual reason for calling, "The time is 12:34, temperature 74 degrees."

I dialed it again right away. It said the exact same time and temperature. I wondered, *Why hasn't the time changed?* I dialed it again right away. It still did not change. I began to panic, the automated time was not changing. I thought, *I'm stuck in time. Time is not changing.* I dialed again. It finally changed to the next minute. I wouldn't allow myself to go to sleep until I realized that the "here and now" were not going to magically change and bring me back to the person I was before June 3, 1989—and that time was still changing. I thought I was caught in a bad dream, and I was about to wake up.

As I replay this phone call scenario in a rational mind, I know that a minute had not passed, but at that time I was not in a thinking, rational state-of-mind. I was relieved when the time changed to the next minute in the message.

I am alive, this is not a dream, I silently thought to myself. This was my reality; time had been standing still, but I didn't understand why.

Often when I was in the hospital, medical staff, and even some family members and friends, would talk to me through my mother as if I wasn't there.

Questions began to flood my brain. *Where am I? Why is everyone talking to me like I am a child. Why aren't people talking to me directly?* The answers were out there; I just didn't know how to ask them. I thought time would begin to stop again if I fell asleep. I was awake for hours. I became frustrated with all the noises, conversations, and people coming in and out—all causing me even more confusion. I could not communicate my thoughts. I had the thoughts, but the words to express them were foreign to me.

Everything went so fast. All of the people rushed around me, not speaking to me, as if I couldn't see them. I felt invisible. Everything was dinging, beeping, buzzing, moving, elevators went up and down, carts squeaked their ways through the halls, nurses came in and nurses went out. There are so many different and strange faces, people around me that I knew, people around me that I didn't know, all speaking to me as if I had seen them before. I would think, *what is that person's name? I know I've seen them before.* Through all of this, there were so many noises. I remember thinking, "*Somebody stop these noises!*"

I didn't realize that my hearing was intensified from the injury (auditory sensitivity), and I couldn't understand why everything appeared as if I were looking in a fun house mirror. My depth perception was so skewed that, as I looked down, everything appeared as though I were looking through a fish bowl. Then as I would raise my head, everything appeared jumbled and mixed up. When I looked at a book, the words were all mixed up, floating around in motion as my eyes moved to focus. I couldn't focus my vision on anything (damage to the visual center of my brain). *Where am I?* I thought, and I remember concluding, *I must be in a mental institution.*

There was a lady down the hall from my room who would constantly scream, "I have to go pee." There were other clues—a hospital smell, nurses walking in and out checking my vitals hourly, doctors discussing me to each other without addressing me as if I weren't in the room or able to participate. There was just an institutional feel to this environment. I was confused. Everyone was careful what they said around me, and too nice to me—to the point that I knew it didn't feel authentic, and they must be getting paid to be interested in me. I can recall thinking, *this place is too clean, and everyone wants to know how I'm feeling.*

As a professional practitioner, I realize now that the therapy sessions were not organized to be client-centered. The sessions were prearranged with an agenda of tasks to complete in the specified fifty-minute sessions of a teaching hospital environment. I could feel the tense, rushed feeling, and I would frequently communicate this feeling with the only expression of communication still alive in my injured brain: my fight instinct. I would have completed the psychological state of fight or flight in more situations than I did, but I could hardly maneuver my body. I wanted to kick and hit people around me. All I could do to express myself was to let out a blood-curdling scream.

My inappropriate behavior was halting my progress toward the goals my therapists had set for me in the required goal plan. Listening to me could have been good practice for my therapists if they had been patient enough not to fill in my long pauses with their own words, and would have just let me make the connections on my own. Instead, I perceived that they treated me as if I were stupid or hard of hearing. I felt as if I was looked upon with pity.

As my confusion grew, I remember thinking *Is this actually happening to me? Why are all of these people concerned about me? Why do they care if I have a bad attitude? Why do they need to know if my poop sank or floated?*

Adding to my confusion were all the decisions I was asked to make. Each one exhausted me. I was asked to make simple choices like, "Do you want a hamburger or tuna fish for lunch?" or "Do you want to wear this nightgown or this tee-shirt?" Even the most basic confused me, like did I want to stand with the walker or stay in my chair while I took a shower? Everything confused me. I wanted someone else to make these decisions for me.

As a practitioner now, I wonder about this: *making decisions is a difficult skill. Could this be why institutional living is the expected living arrangement for many recovering survivors of TBI—because they simply lack the self-monitoring skills?*

Everything and every second are all micro-managed, planned, scheduled, and then given to the patient in a hospital or residential care facility environment. As a result, the patient is not forced to make rehabilitative interventions, or to learn how to make wise decisions on their own. Thus, thinking, expressing, and evaluating the situation are not forced upon them. This disables the skill, allowing the person to exist without having any input or their feelings addressed.

I was empty, a shell of my once-captivating personality. That was gone. I couldn't remember anything. There were pictures of me at different stages of my life placed at my eye-level in the hospital room. Mom placed them there deliberately to assist me in making connections to my past.

The confusing world was happening all around me, sending me spinning, screaming, and hitting. I didn't realize then that this stubborn attitude, combined with just the right mixture in my genetics, is essential in the "fight." Looking back, I guess there are times when being a bitch has its benefits.

~Chapter Four~

Modeling Days

How did I get to the intersection where my life was to change so dramatically?

I was emotionally strapped in an unhealthy relationship at the time. After five years of incarceration, my fiancee, Steve, had just rented a house and it quickly became the setting for many of our arguments. One night, following yet another of our disagreements, I didn't bother with strapping on my seat belt in my hurry to get some distance between us. Perhaps this restraint could have reduced my injury, but I will never know. What I do know is that before my brain damage the word "restraint" was just not a part of my vocabulary.

I had lived with Steve after his arrest and throughout his trial. Then he was moved to Texas to serve his time. I moved to Dallas to be closer to him, to visit him in jail, and to live my dream of becoming a top fashion model. Steve had put a large down payment on the car that almost claimed my life four years later. His plan was to provide me with reliable transportation, so I could visit him while he was incarcerated. Eventually, he was transferred to another penitentiary in Minnesota, served the remainder of his time, and moved back to Missouri.

My clothing and a small amount of furniture was all I possessed. It seemed that everything I had with me in Dallas was not mine but just loaned to me by Steve.

The car I drove had side-panel damage due to a minor accident in Dallas. A sly man who worked in the auto-repair business promised me that he could repair the dent and give it a new paint job. I didn't think to ask him if he had a paint booth in his shop. I don't even think where I met him was his shop, but I trusted him. I was a twenty-year-old woman, trying to survive by myself in an unfamiliar city. I had no experience in the area of auto body repair schemes. As a result, my shiny new car had several patches of mosquitoes embedded in the paint, and the side panel was not repaired properly. Shortly after this con man made his money, I moved back to Missouri to get away from Steve and reclaim my life.

Steve and I at the minimum
security prison in Texas, jokingly
referred to by some as "Club Fed."

I had very little modeling work after my move back from Dallas. I switched careers and took a six-month course to become a travel agent instead. I was used to earning more money than this, so I took a second job working nights as a cocktail waitress at a nearby hotel.

On the trip back from Dallas, I drove nonstop, except for bathroom breaks and food or fuel requirements. At a stop for fuel, I remember I was excited and couldn't wait to tell someone about something unusual that had just happened during my late night traveling.

Just as any other bored, highway-weary driver, I was flipping through the available (mostly country western) radio stations. A song was playing telling a story of a husband and wife splitting up their possessions after a divorce settlement. The cause of their divorce was a parrot that had told the wife of another woman being with her husband. The chorus had a line that said, "The last thing she gave me was the 'bird'."

Just as the word 'bird' was sung in a slow country twang, a bird crashed into my windshield. After cleaning up the mess, I had such a good time telling the tired, old gas station attendant my story. In retrospect, perhaps this was a sign or an omen of what was to come in my near future. Instead of a bird, it would be *me* that crashed into the windshield.

Ten hours after I left Dallas, I arrived back in home territory where everything was familiar. I didn't have a thing to my name but the once-cute-and-sleek, little sports car.

It was this sports car in which my life-changing accident would later take place. My sister Nancy explained to me on her questionnaire that minutes before the accident, I had called her crying about an argument that Steve and I were having. I have no memory of the argument, but I do recall having had thoughts of totaling my car before it really happened. I never imagined totaling my entire life and everything I had ever worked for.

I must have been suicidal. I know I was depressed. I placed all of my energy on my external appearance, ignoring the development of my internal being. I wouldn't allow myself to eat anything fattening. I refused to acknowledge that my body frame or genetic make-up guaranteed that I would be naturally thin. Steve would comment about my double chin as he bought me a candy bar. I was so young and easily influenced by the mixed messages he was sending. I can only assume that he must have seen his father treat his mother this confusing way. These mixed messages could have been what drove his mother into doing the unimaginable and taking her own life.

I had an unrealistic idea of beauty. I tried to become what the market wanted. It seemed to me that all the modeling jobs were going to the models with blonde hair and blue eyes, the "All-American look." All I had was my "look," and that wasn't enough. My agent suggested I go to Milan, Italy to model where my "look" was marketable, and I could get work. I let this hurt how I perceived myself. I translated that into a feeling that I could not live up to others' expectations.

I remember having thoughts before that night in June, of driving my car into a garage and going to sleep. I never planned a time or a date to carry out this selfish plan, but Steve's mother had carried out that very plan. I don't remember the specifics of her situation, and I refuse to research the grim details.

I remember her as being very beautiful from the pictures Steve had shown me. She was maybe in her late thirties, and a successful partner in a restaurant. I believe Steve was eleven at the time, and that he was deeply affected throughout his life by the tragic early death of his mother.

Now, I realize that the past is in the past. We cannot change what has happened, and we cannot change the inevitable, but we can change what will happen today by the attitude we decide to carry. I accept responsibility for what I let him do to my self-esteem, but I have left the past in the past.

Searching for
the perfect
headshot. Taken
by professional
photographer Jim
Goss of Kansas City,
Missouri in 1986.

~CHAPTER FIVE~

Conventional Therapy

The blow to my head had reduced my ability to discern what was outside from what was inside. I began regaining consciousness in the most primitive part of my brain first. When I was hungry, I wanted food right then. When I smelled something familiar, I would have a memory. When my extra-sensitive hearing became overstimulated, I would lash out at the noise. To help me deal with this confusion, I went to intensive therapies.

First each day, I had speech therapy, followed by physical therapy (PT), and finally ending my day with occupational therapy (OT). Speech therapy bombarded me with the same questions over and over, and with picture-matching games that seemed intended for a toddler. PT insisted that I do exercises that had been a mere warm-up activity to the hours I used to give to the stair machine, weight training circuit, or other aerobic activities. Instead, I would do arm chair activities, and raise my arm twenty times or my leg ten times, or ride a stationary bike for ten minutes, just to make the therapist happy. I had to look pleased, as if I were responding to their usual enthusiastic spiel with equally enthusiastic responses. "Come on you can do it!" they would say, "Yeah, that's what we want to see, good job."

OT gave me even more insight into what I couldn't do with my arm and hand, like grasping objects at waist level or prying my right arm away from my side. I went to therapy each day while in the hospital, trying my hardest, in fifty-minute intervals, to make all my therapists happy. This was exhausting!

I especially hated OT; it seemed particularly degrading. The therapist asked me to do mindless activities that a child could do, but I was unable do them. I could smell the therapist's breath, and it made me sick. I smelled her body odor also. My physical therapist smelled like a familiar perfume. I liked that smell. But my OT smelled like a wax, kind of a plastic smell. I didn't like that smell.

All the therapies were frustrating, but OT seemed especially so. I had lost complete use of my right arm and hand, and I was continually being asked to do things that I could no longer do. I became more and more impatient as each OT session wore on.

One day as I was leaving to go therapy, my sister Debbie asked me over the phone what I would like to eat when I got done. In my broken-up speech, grunting like a starving caveman, I said, "Beef and bean burrito."

In response to my questionnaire, Debbie recalled her memories of this day, "She had to start physical therapy after she had lain there for about a month. I'm not sure when she started talking, but there were just a few words in her vocabulary at first. One day, I had told her I would bring her some food to the hospital for lunch. By this time the hospital food was really gross to her. She said, 'Beef and bean burrito.' She always loved Mexican food. My Becky was coming back!

"When she was in therapy," Debbie continued, "she got mad at the therapist, and hit her. She knew that I was bringing her lunch that day, and the therapist was making her late to meet me. That freaked me out because Becky was never a violent person. She always had really bad PMS, but she never was overtly violent. She could be a bitch at times, but it was usually PMS-related. I still joke around with her about how she said, 'Beef and bean burrito.' That was a real turning point. She was talking and she was asking for familiar things."

I don't know if I lashed out with violence because I was tired and hungry, or if my sense of smell had overpowered my ability to be polite.

Maybe it was just because she was the last therapy of the day, and I couldn't put words to my frustration. Or perhaps, I just wanted to cut out of therapy early for that burrito my sister had promised me. Whatever the motivation, I used my strong left fist to punch my therapist several times in quick succession. I had no difficulty maneuvering my left side!

During my stay at the hospital, I proved my left arm to be quick on another occasion as well. One of these was when Mom took me down to the hospital coffee shop for a sandwich as a break from the bland hospital food. It was impossible to embarrass my mother, but when I was functioning out of my primitive, animal brain, I guess I came pretty close. It was a warm summer day. I don't remember much else about the day, except that I was hot while we were waiting for our food. As sweat was beading up on my nose, I reached over my head and around my shoulder to my back with my left hand, and off went my shirt.

I enjoyed a few seconds of satisfying coolness before mom, exhibiting her own brand of coolness, reached over to replace my shirt. Like I said, it was pretty hard to embarrass Mom.

I was extra-sensitive to all the alarms and whistles that constantly go off in the daily routine of a hospital. Once I realized that it was safe to go to sleep and that I would be waking up each morning, I needed silence to drift off. That was hard to come by. I would kick my mom, who slept in a cot at the end of my bed, to tell her I was not asleep yet. Her snoring was louder than all the hospital buzzers, intercoms, and ringing noises combined. I could at least control one noise in my environment. My poor sleep-deprived mother!

At this point in my recovery, says Carl, "Rebekah communicated first by writing awkwardly with her left hand (her right was paralyzed). As I recall, one of the first things she wrote was 'NOT CRAZY.'

"As far as I know," he says, "I heard her first words after the accident. She was sitting in her hospital room, and I was there keeping up a monologue when she began tapping her foot and staring at me. That was her signal that she wanted something. I asked whether she wanted a drink or needed me to help her to the bathroom or what. But she only stared at me harder. I said, 'I'll help you, but you have to tell me what you want.' She whispered, 'I want to go to the bathroom.' She showed no recognition that this was a major breakthrough, but I was ecstatic.

"Sharon and I tried to fix these milestones in her memory," Carl continues, "so she wouldn't slide back and have to work her way forward again. We'd often celebrate with Hägen Dazs bars. We all used humor to help us through the days. For example, I remember 'square dancing' with her using only our forefingers to shape a square."

During this time, I didn't know how to control much of anything. I had learned that letting out my brand of blood-curdling screams would quiet down any environment. My screaming became a replacement for the words I could not find. When my hospital room would become too active, I would scream; when therapy would become too demanding, I would scream. I screamed when I was hungry, tired, and frustrated by my inability to understand or remember how to interact with people, places, or things in my environment.

Testing by my speech therapist just before my discharge from the hospital proved that I knew Jimmy Carter was not president in August of 1989 and that I was twenty-two, not twelve. These had been my responses for quite some time before I started to connect the dots, so to speak.

I communicated freely some entertaining thoughts to my speech therapist. Once, when she was testing my ability to reason, she asked me one of her routine questions: "What would you do if you were on vacation and lost your purse?" This was the first question I remembered. I told her without a doubt, "I would hitchhike home."

Rehabilitation was a long ride, and I couldn't hitchhike. The motivation was all up to me.

Two pictures taken in the hospital's Rehabilitation Unit: the last stop in what I like to call my "summer vacation." The right side of my body is partially paralyzed as I attempt a smile for Mom behind the camera.

~CHAPTER SIX~

Life as Therapy

Doctor's letter of disability given on release from hospital:

Sharon Eiker has asked that I relay a medical report to you regarding Rebekah Dyer for purposes of assessing her condition limitations and prognosis.

Rebekah Dyer was admitted to the Emergency Room at St. Luke's Hospital on 6/3/89 after being involved in a motor vehicle accident. She was found to have closed head injury with MRI scan evidences of right frontal, right temporal contusions, left frontal contusion, left cerebral peduncle contusion and multiple sites of contusion including cerebella and other cerebral areas. In addition, she was found to have fractures of her clavicle bilaterally and fluid levels in the left maxillary sinus and sphenoid sinuses. The patient is currently an inpatient on the Rehabilitation Unit at St. Luke's Hospital. Utilizing the functional index score, she presently has a score of 67 out of a possible 126 still requiring assistance in feeding, grooming, bathing, dressing, toileting. She requires assistance in bowel and bladder management. She requires supervision for transfer skill, toilet transfer and tub and shower transfer. She requires moderate assistance of an attendant in locomotion and stairs. In her thinking skills, she does not recall the accident. She is becoming more alert to individuals and does remember names of examiners from day to day. Does remember most of the names of her family and friends. She does not have a full understanding of the implications of her injuries. She has bursts of anger that she has difficulty controlling. She is beginning to speak and only for the past week has been able to voice. She continues to have a complete paralysis of her right arm and a partial paralysis of her right leg.

Regarding her mental capabilities, she has some understanding of her self and those about her, but little capability to judge implications. Thinking is very concrete and deals principally with the immediate. She is not making plans and does not take into consideration her various impairments in her planning.

Toward the future I expect her to improve in her locomotion skills, her speaking skills. I expect her to be amnesic for the period of the accident and probably most of the period of time in the hospital. She does have the potential to improve over approximately a twelve to eighteen month period, but it is common for head injured individuals to have long standing deficits in memory, judgement, planning and other more subtle higher cognitive skills. These will require assessment in the future. For the immediate, she does require the assistance of other individuals in making decisions, in my opinion.

I really didn't know where my ruby red slippers were, why I was there, where the tornado hit, or where I was going next in this great land of Oz. From repetition and routine with dedicated therapists, I slowly began to think in a sequential manner. In speech therapy each day, I would respond to similar groups of questions and activities. I grew tired of hearing the same things, but I suppose it was the daily repetition of the therapy sessions, and my family trying to help me remember who I was, that helped me slowly piece all of the events together.

I did recognize faces but names were hard for me—even names of my own family. I worked hard to appear as if I weren't confused, so I avoided addressing people by their names whenever I could. I thought I was going to be just fine, but I wasn't able to hide my feelings. I would just blurt out whatever I was thinking.

I have learned much about the brain and all of the technical terms for different impairments. The word used by professionals for loss of ability to recognize familiar objects is agnosia. This is a result of damage or impairment caused by stroke or brain injury to the medial occipitotemporal cortex. When referring specifically to the face, a person could use the term *prosopagnosia* (derived from the Greek words *prospopon* for face, and *agnosia* for not knowing) for the inability to recognize faces. The person affected by this condition could have difficulty recognizing even people very close to them.

Family and friends of a person who has experienced brain damage should never take recognition or naming difficulties personally. It is not that the injured are stupid, will always not recognize you, or must have forgotten that they loved you; it is simply a problem resulting from damage to the brain.

Through therapy, the affected person can learn to use different ways to remember people and names. I use word association to help with this challenge. I think of something that the person reminds me of. I know a person who has experienced a TBI that calls an acquaintance of ours "Green Bean." Whatever works! This condition will get better and better through repetition and as time heals the brain.

As I studied about the brain post-injury, I thought that I had escaped experiencing what some people have to endure: Capgra's syndrome, which is caused by damage to the temporal lobe. The person experiencing this disorder recognizes the family member or friend, but has no emotional connection to them and usually thinks that they are meeting an imposter of their loved one. I did experience a level of prosopagnosia that was similar to Capgra's syndrome, but it was not quite the same. Like Capgra's syndrome, I felt no emotions for a friend to whom I had once been quite close; but unlike Capgra's, I also did not know who he was when he called and visited me. For that loss, I am truly sorry. Just six months earlier, he had taken me to the island of Maui in Hawaii. After our awkward visit in the hospital, he disappeared from my life, but he thoughtfully left the photos of our trip together (shown below).

Damage to the brain is so mysterious that a doctor, with all his hard-earned education, cannot tell you what capabilities will be diminished or altered for the survivor to have to deal with for the rest of her life. A doctor cannot tell whether a person in a coma will be unconscious for an hour, a day, weeks, or even years. A doctor is unable to pinpoint which of the survivor's five senses could be affected permanently, temporarily, or not at all. For years I was unable to cry and when I finally did, I was so happy about the tears forming in my eyes that they dried up.

Anything could have happened should I have had further damage and experienced more swelling of my brain. I don't mean to make it sound like I don't think doctors can do much, or that I'm not grateful for their help; doctors are skilled at performing interventions, during the crucial window of time, that can save lives and reduce disability. Furthermore, the rehabilitation, neurology and medical doctors are essential to a survivor maintaining a quality life post-TBI. They can prescribe medications or suggest therapies to help through the recovery process.

Nancy said she knew I was becoming more aware of my environment the day I saw myself in a mirror.

"Once we went to the bathroom," Nancy writes, "and I say 'we' because you couldn't walk by yourself. You caught a glimpse of yourself in the mirror, and I have to say, I've never seen you stare so hard in the mirror before. I had to pull you away from the mirror. You really enjoyed having blush put on your cheeks, and it reminded me of petting a cat. You were practically purring."

As Nancy told me this, I recalled what I was feeling that day. I remembered how I couldn't wait to cover up the dark circles under my eyes and to use a little blush, lipstick and mascara. Also a razor, for the European "natural" look I'd acquired on my legs and underarms. Make-up can only make a person look better though, as they continue to do the therapy; it does not "make up" for all of the abilities lost through TBI.

Unfortunately, there was no cream or cover-up that could help me accept my sudden awareness of reality. I was in a hospital and about to go home. Where was home? I was afraid to ask.

I have a lot of jumbled and lost memories, but I did remember that my mom did not like Steve. There was tension in the room as we covered up this reality whenever he would come to visit me in the hospital. I also had confusion if there was too much activity around me.

The frontal lobes control your inhibitions. Sarah recalls a time when I bit her on the head. I don't remember doing this, but I do remember her being around and bored. When there is an insult to the frontal lobe area of the brain, it affects the ability to control the "gatekeeper," or sort of a "compass" so-to-speak. This area controls your true feelings. I had no problems telling the truth after the accident, although it wasn't always taken as just "telling the truth."

Due to my frontal lobe damage, a certain lack of inhibition guided which stories I chose daily to entertain my therapists with while I was an inpatient. They knew everything about me, from my mom's loud snoring to my boyfriends wanting me to do nasty things with them. I would even pick my nose in front of strangers as if they weren't there. The gatekeeper mechanism just wasn't intact in my frontal lobes. I wasn't able to play the game of life. I wasn't able to say, "I love you, too." That would have been the correct thing to say to my boyfriend turned "just friend" who was attempting to visit me in the hospital. Perhaps choosing to say it could have allowed positive movement in my life with the least amount of effort. But I guess he was not "in-the-cards," of my luck. The game of life had dealt me a difficult hand of cards, and as I was discarding, the "Dealer" had no pity. He dealt me cards from the "challenging deck."

My sister Debbie reminded me of the day I was discharged from the hospital: "Mom, Sarah, Rebekah and I were all in the car. Our Becky was alive, talking and walking. All the things the doctors said she would never do again, she had accomplished. I'll never trust a doctor's opinion again. The day she got out of the hospital, she was in a wheel chair, but she had taken a few steps. When we were leaving the hospital, she was singing a song that came on the radio and knew the words. There was hope for my Becky."

When a patient gets discharged from the hospital, there is usually an environment that the former patient is released to from the hospital's care. In this one place, they may have their personal belongings and can have a sense of where they belong. I didn't have such a "homecoming." I experienced more confusion. I went to my sister Nancy's home while my mother fixed up a room for me in her urban, midtown home. I didn't know that staying at Nancy's was only temporary. I only knew what was in front of me, and the view was confusing. I couldn't find the words to express what I felt. I was lost in the experience of the "here and now."

Nancy shared this to help me remember this homecoming: "You stayed with us for about five days in our front bedroom. When we arrived home, you were very hungry, and I asked you what you wanted to eat. You said, 'a bean B-U-R-R-I-T-O from Taco Bell.' You pronounced all the letters in burrito, slowly and fairly well. As if you wanted to make sure that it was very clear what you wanted."

The next thing I recall is being on a road trip with my mom and two of my sisters. Still no home to go to, I had no independence and was out of control of my own destiny.

Before my brain was slammed into the car frame, I was a different person. Becky Dyer had graduated from high school at age 17, always being driven, working three jobs, and in control of all plans for the future. Suddenly at 22, I could hardly walk or talk. I was using a wheelchair, as well as arm, leg, and shoulder braces to maneuver through a greatly reduced activity level. But Mom didn't let this slight detour ruin her summer plans. She packed us all in her 1981 Eldorado Cadillac, and we hit the road for Pensacola, Florida.

This would be a road trip unlike any other we had taken, even though I had been raised driving coast-to-coast and was accustomed to this type of journey with my family. These somewhat unusual summer vacation trips were very special childhood memories.

We would pack up our gear in a blue and white VW hippy van with no air conditioning, sweating on our siblings and eating out of an army trunk filled with basics such as peanut butter, bread, tuna, ramen noodles, potato chips, cooking oil, bananas, captain crunch cereal for my brother and raisin bran for everyone else. A cooler full of milk, mayonnaise, ham, cheese, eggs, bacon, and apples rounded out the rest of the menu. We went camping throughout the U.S., at times without all the appropriate gear and with frequent transportation breakdowns.

I recall one of these trips as a young girl when we drove through San Francisco without a reverse gear. Envision a van full of kids ranging from 8 to 14-years-old, and a mom with stop sign-shaped glasses, descending one of those steep hills for which San Francisco is famous and getting stuck at the bottom. Then imagine four skinny kids pushing this van up the hill, just enough to be able to jump-start it and then whip a U-turn, so we could make it back up the hill. This was my memory of San Francisco at 8-years-old: never go down a dead end hill! This van was our only transportation for many years. Then suddenly one summer, the trips took on a different challenge with a disabled passenger.

Our summer road trip was not lacking in excitement, even though we had a working vehicle this time. Just different. Our

Becky behind the "hippy van" imitating Richard Nixon!

survival gear was different for one thing: wheelchair, medications, braces, and all the equipment needed for my newly disabled body packed up in our all-leather interior, beautiful car.
This car was a gift to mom from her ex-husband, the one we
were traveling to visit.

Even in our great anticipation of reaching the ocean, though,
we took a detour for a stop in New Orleans. We had all our personal items packed tightly to survive this week-long visit to the
South. When we arrived, and had located a parking space along
a busy street, we went out for a stroll and roll through the French
Quarter. We had a great time: listening to Cajun music, drinking
chicory-thick coffee, talking to locals, and learning about life by
talking to the street performers in this part of our county.

Once we had sipped in enough of the atmosphere to satisfy our thirst, we returned to the place where we had left our
beautiful car. My sister Nancy and Mother simultaneously said,
"Where is our car?"

It was not there. Our car had been stolen! All of our belongings were gone. Mom called the police and was told that she would have to report this crime at the police station in person. She told them of our unique circumstances and how her disabled daughter was in a wheelchair. This did not move the police at all in the decision of how their priorities should be ordered. The police would not come to help us. Apparently, this was not a crime earning emergency status, so we had to walk and roll there on our own.

The therapeutic value of such a trip cannot be measured in a traditional fashion and charted on a graph to prove its efficacy. I can only say that the experience sure left an impression on me.

My 5'6" mom, pushing my wheelchair down the middle of the dark streets of New Orleans with a hot, humid breeze pushing back my long, naturally curly, dark brown hair, is quite a picture, isn't it? We didn't know where we were or what was on the next block of houses. We anticipated the description that Mom gave us on our survival-based hunt for the dark-red brick building of the police station. Mother was making the best out of a bad situation, singing songs, and trying not to show her anxiety. Thankfully, it was not too far, eight blocks or so. The police station was full of people yelling, uniformed officers, and uniquely dressed people with heavy make-up—all proclaiming their innocence.

This entertaining diversion didn't end our summer vacation either. Mother wouldn't let the thoughtless thieves shipwreck our summer. We took a Greyhound bus for the remaining distance to Pensacola, Florida, to visit the stepdad I barely knew. I was innocently following along, without a doubt in my mind that we were going to make it to our destination, until nature called. It was time. No matter what; I had to use the restroom.

The bathroom was all the way in the back of the bus. There was no way to wait; I had to make the journey into the dark.

Lights were illuminating several of the occupied seats, as people were busy talking or reading. The goal was the blue light that read, RESTROOM. My instability made it seem like a city block to travel this length, *all* of the seats, to the back of the moving bus. After discussion with my mother, I stood up. My newly injured right side had to depend on my uninjured left to carry my entire body. I was thrown off balance. As I would place my weight onto my right leg, my right knee would jerk my entire body as the overextension of weak muscles snapped my knee back into place. Down the aisle I struggled. I leaned forward with all my effort, grasping for the next seat on the bus, I boosted myself forward with my only working arm and hand, pulling myself to the next seat, only to have to repeat the cycle. Each seat was occupied by a set of eyes, looking up at me with sympathy or curiosity.

When I finally reached the bathroom, the door was locked. By this time, I *really* had to "go." My older sister Nancy, who had supervised me during this heroic effort, calmly said, "Okay, we'll just wait until the person finishes and opens the door."

I waited and I knocked. I waited and I knocked. No matter what the effort, my impatience grew, and there was still no response. A person sitting close to us replied, "I don't think I've seen anyone go in or come out."

Nancy took the initiative; she left me in the back of the bus and went to tell the bus driver of our problem. She politely asked the bus driver, "Could you please unlock the door for my disabled sister?"

The countdown was on. Every second she was gone, I was tapping my feet and sharing my impatience with my fellow passengers. No one spoke to me as I sat in the back row. I felt a sense of being purposely ignored, like a homeless person begging strangers for change. I watched as Nancy finally began her return to the back of the bus. All of the eyes glanced up at her with approval and sympathy as she briskly walked by, leaving a cool breeze on each set of eyes.

She reported to me, "The driver told me that you will have to wait until the next stop." I felt my blood boil with anger, creating an uncontrollable steam that soon reached the top of my head and released itself in a scream. It was a scream that would have made waves had there been water around me, like the water rippling around an alligator as it lets out its bellowing growl before it snaps on its prey.

Needless to say, this alerted our driver to pull over the Greyhound bus and unlock the door to allow me to use the bathroom, with not a second to delay. In the end, the only snapping *this* alligator did was the unclasping of my jeans, followed by the relaxing, rushing of a waterfall echoing in the latrine.

Going to the ocean wasn't enough for Mom. She also wanted the healing energy of the mountains for her daughter. We drove through the mountains of Colorado, in a green Dodge pickup truck, our gear in the back covered securely with a green tarp. We sang songs to divert our anxiety as we crept up the next set of inclines in the Rockies. My little sister and I would simultaneously lean forward instinctively in our effort to encourage the truck to reach the top. I'll never forget the opportunity I had to sit in the back, wedged in among the gear as we curved through the mountain roads, listening to my lifelong favorite song: Pink Floyd's "Comfortably Numb."

When we stopped for the night to camp in the Rockies, we picked out a rustic camping spot. With no wood to be had but dead fallen branches, my resourceful mother built a huge fire to warm up a cup of cocoa. I guess I couldn't get close enough to the warmth: the chair gave out and down I went into the fire. Mom jumped over the picnic table and pulled me out. I wrote about the incident later in my journal.

Mom had started me on keeping a journal right after our trip to Florida. She set up a manual typewriter and insisted that I record my thoughts daily. At first, I could write no more than, "I can't remember what happened today." Later on, I started keeping a journal by hand in an effort to improve my penmanship using my non-dominate left hand.

April 6, 1990 Friday
    A day after Moms B-day. My first journal entry, handwritten, because, the tape went bad on the typewritter. My kitten, Charlie, has been sick. He seems to be getting better though. Thank God! I have a test tomarrow, then, Micheal, Nancy, Jeffery, and I are going to Marshall for Mark Krauss wedding. I'm really looking foward to it. Micheal gets to meet my whole family. I said to Mary, "I hope you guys like him." She said, "I'm sure we will." I said, "well If Mom does I'm sure you will, because, she's the hard one to convince."

Above: My first hand-written journal entry.

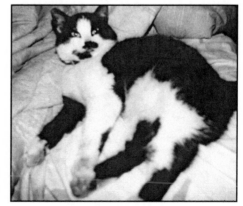

Right: Charlie Chaplin (CC) at the Eiker House

This is how my journal entries read during the Colorado leg of our trip:

Saturday August 4, 1990

"In Colorado at a campsite. Talk about rustic. Last night I slept a total of maybe 2 hrs. & then today we drove around trying to find this campsite that has latrines and no shower houses. We have to go and get any water. I was in a really bad mood when we got here because it was raining and we had to set up camp and I was starving. I haven't shit for three days. My stomach hurts. Sarah's being weird.

"Miss Know-it-all" can't ever possibly be wrong. She's getting on my nerves. We're out in the wilderness way up in the mountains. It's freezing too. I did not come prepared. I brought stuff for a camp in KC.

Monday the 6th of August

Still camping beautiful surroundings. I'm in a much better mood than I was after that drive through Kansas. It's beautiful here but cold at night. We switched camps today. This one doesn't have RV's so it's better. We have a perfect view of the mountains.

Thursday 9, August

I haven't written in here for a couple of days so I'll try to catch up.

Tuesday

Went on a trail with Sarah. Went to Boulder rode in the back of the truck. What a beautiful view!!!

Wednesday

Boulder what a great town. Bought some really loud pants. Went to eat at a Chinese restaurant all of us ate for $8.50 but the way me & mom tip it was probably about $12.00. I fell in the fire I went down to pick up my hot chocolate & the chair gave out on me. I have a burn on my wrist & elbow the lady across the way had a first aid kit. We need to get one. Things could have been a lot worse. Mom pulled me out real quick. If she hadn't of my hair could of burnt. Boy it was really traumatic. We're moving camp today so I need to help. We're moving to Cherry Creek Reservoir.
Well, we moved camp this one is a bit more not so primitive. Has a beach on a lake a shower house, laundry facilities. Back to civilization we go. I helped mom read a map successfully. This has been a great vacation. I just read about high altitude sickness. I had that on Saturday & Sunday.

Above left: Trying to cool off after helping to set up camp where I later fell into the fire.

Above right: Using car door as a crutch on the Florida trip.

Below: Mom relaxes on a Colorado overlook.

Above: Mom and I on another overlook.

Friday 10 of August

At Cherry Creek went swimming all day today.
I got quite a bit of sun. Then we went to the mall
outside of Denver called Arapahoe plaza. After we
went and ate at the mall we drove on the dam.
Darn, last day of camping. We're staying at the
holiday Inn in Denver. So we have to pack up I'm
not looking forward to that work. This has been
nice. Sarah's out riding her bike it's almost dark so
she should be coming home. Hopefully, it is just me,
because I'm worried and Mom is gone to take a
shower.

What we have planned so far is the Zoo tomorrow
then the gallery on Sunday & then home on Monday.
We should be home in time to go to Dr. Burgess's
appt. I will have a lot of things to talk about in
therapy. I also want to get my nails done. My burn
has pretty much scabbed over it's a big sore. I'm sure
Sarah is all right she must have met some people &
lost track of time. I'm sitting here at Cherry Creek
Reservoir.

August 12, Sunday

We're at the Holiday Inn. We switched rooms
because we could not see outside. We watched a
couple of movies "New York Stories" A Betty Davis
movie" some more.

I introduce and address myself as "Rebekah"

hoping that dropping the nickname would help people realize the transformation that took place. I'm sure no one put this together, but it helps me.

August 19, 1990

I've gone through a major awakening. Your friends most likely don't ever become a completely changed person, especially for the better. A person never changes unless something life threatening happens like a close to death experience

My personal treatment plan had already begun while we were enjoying our vacation, even though I didn't realize it at the time. I didn't go to a rehabilitation facility like the doctors had suggested to my mother during the discharge planning meeting and, fortunately for my daughters, neither did my mother follow their advice to have me sterilized. This is routinely suggested to the parents of young girls after a head injury because of their lack of inhibitions and difficulty with complex thought processes.

The intervention of the Florida vacation served to get me in a car again. Then, once we got to Pensacola, I had to develop the strength to walk up the long flight of stairs each day to my stepdad's apartment, near the Navy base where he worked as a scientist.

The milestones of recovery continued. While in my stepfather's very small apartment my coffee was seemingly magically filled to the brim. Mom asked me, "How did you fill up your coffee from across the room?" So I was motivated by my coffee cup, empty for too long, to take my first independent steps.

When we visited the beautiful, salty water of the ocean, I was able only with my mom's assistance to get out to the beach and feel the sand squish through my toes as the waves repeatedly crashed to knock us down. I also learned how embarrassing it is to scream in public, but that didn't stop me.

Nancy, Rebekah, and Sarah in Stepfather's Florida apartment where the "coffee cup miracle" took place!

Sitting with "Mama Bear" on the beach in Pesacola, Fl.

In the outdoor shower with Sarah at the beach.

~CHAPTER SEVEN~

Unwrapping My Memories

A person who acquires a traumatic brain injury typically leaves the hospital and goes directly to another institution to continue therapy. The survivor lives amongst others with similar injuries, waiting to be rehabilitated back into society. My destiny didn't follow such a linear fashion. Everyday life was to be my therapy, with my mother as my case manager. While I was still in the hospital, a team meeting was held in which every available discipline was represented: a speech therapist, occupational therapist, and physical therapist, as well as the lead nurse case manager, a rehabilitation physician and a social worker were all present. Afterwards, the professionals told my family that I would not be returning to living independently, so Nancy and my brother-in-law Jeff packed up my studio apartment.

When we got back to Kansas City from our whirlwind tour of the South, I was moved into Mom's house. Finally, all my familiar things came out of storage. I was even allowed to view my wrecked car in a parking lot before it was hauled off. Although memories were rapidly making connections, I felt no emotional response when I saw this unrecognizable mess of metal.

Unpacking the boxes from storage was just like Christmas. I knew that I liked all of these things, and that they were mine to keep. I cannot describe the feelings I had to finally be able to sleep in my own bed and to be around all my familiar possessions. When the day finally arrived to unpack, it felt like when you're four-years-old and still believe in Santa Claus: you lie awake anticipating the bells and hooves of reindeer carrying the sleigh of toys for Christmas morning.

How did they get the list of all of these things that I remembered and wanted? Memories began flooding in: the feel of my clothes, my shoes, my sheets, my comforter and pillow. I began to remember where I had bought my perfume, make-up, and earrings. The smells connected memories to places I had once visited, and people I had once known. This was now to be my home for the next four years.

During this time of rapid development, Nancy wrote letters to our family around the U.S., updating them all on my recovery. I happened upon this one dated September 26, 1989:

Dear Family,

Usually on Sundays I've been visiting for extended periods of time over at Sharon Eiker's home where Becky has been convalescing. My Mom (Sharon) has a very big home in Kansas City, for those of you who did not know. Becky has recently learned how to walk in small steps and can also make it up and down stairs in most cases. Three times each week Becky goes to the hospital to perform therapy and she is doing remarkably well. It is hard to believe but Becky can actually lift her right arm and shake hands now.

As you recall there was uncertainty whether Becky was ever going to be able to use her right arm again. Her speech is coming along very well as well. It's interesting how her topic of conversation has changed and is noticeably more meaningful than it was previous to her accident. I hope all is well with everyone and that you are being extra careful when you are driving.

Love,

Nancy Williams

~CHAPTER EIGHT~

Unattended Steps

Once a person begins to show signs of improvement, services are discontinued. Independent Living Centers (ILCs) can be a logical choice for service delivery to persons with brain injury because they are not time-limited. They believe all people with disabilities deserve human rights, and the ILC understands how to access benefits from a variety of systems such as Social Security and Vocational Rehabilitation.

My research in the year 2000 on this subject made me aware of the need for further investigation in TBI literature on the long-term outcome of services provided. This is a topic that will be examined for many years to come. It is difficult to change the long-held belief systems of the general public. Many people can not make the shift in thought. They believe that being surrounded by technology and professionals equals protection, and families logically want their loved one to stay in this protective environment. Generally, a family just doesn't want to see their loved one fail after living through such a traumatic experience. The family, professionals, and the survivor should all have one goal in mind, and that is taking the necessary steps to lead the person to a fulfilling life after a TBI.

One service that is available to those who qualify is a Head Injury Waiver, which is now being provided by an increasing number of states in the U.S. This may provide a number of different alternatives. The environment that we live in today: the number of persons with brain injuries, the assumptions being made about them, and the move toward shorter hospital stays have all resulted in many people struggling to design services that meet the lifetime needs of persons with brain injuries. It may be the person down the street or the "cousin of," or a "friend of," but it seems to me that everyone now knows of a person or has heard of a person who has experienced a traumatic brain injury. This is a person who wishes to be on his own, to be able to do things for himself without the need for services, to grow toward a meaningful life and to be seen as a contributing member of society.

These are themes throughout many people's lives. Why should it be any different for a person who has been thrust into a situation they'd never planned on? We aren't so different, "just a little tweaked," as my brother Sam says.

As I began this new, unplanned stage in my life, I would attend pool therapy, speech, occupational, and physical therapy sessions each Monday, Wednesday and Friday. With delight, my first unattended steps—since the two I had taken in my stepdad's apartment to refill my coffee cup—were in the pool. I felt like I could walk with the walls of water around me, but once I ascended out of the water afterwards I could feel the weight of gravity taking its toll on my body once again, dragging me down and making me struggle to find my sense of balance. This was an exhausting regimen. I later was interviewed on the news about helping the staff at St. Luke's develop an aerobics class for people in physical therapy.

I worked hard at regaining the ability to do everyday activities, and we attempted a number of different ways to make my therapy seem like real life. The staff would take me out to the bus stop, explain where we were going and ride around with me, observing my behaviors as people shoved each other on the bus.

Having lunch at a restaurant was also one of my therapy outings. After all, disrobing at the table because you're hot isn't approved of socially. I got away with it in the hospital coffee shop, but society generally frowns on such behavior!

The therapists believed in my ability to behave appropriately and rewarded me by taking me to my favorite hamburger joint. They monitored my social behavior and did their best to provide a calm experience for me. I had forgotten what I liked to order, so I tried to read the menu in an effort to make the memory come back. This frustrated me, but otherwise everything went smoothly. Things weren't so calm when my mom took me on such an outing.

I treated therapy like a job. At a job, you typically get two fifteen-minute breaks and a thirty-minute lunch in an eight-hour day. On this particular afternoon, however, I didn't take a lunch break. In fact, I worked through all of my breaks.

A person who has experienced a brain trauma gets grouchy toward the end of the day if her basic needs aren't met—like, for example, resting and eating. I had spent all day performing for my therapists, and I was tired and hungry. Mom decided to treat me to a lunch out at a local diner.

The restaurant was busy, and we had to wait our turn to be seated and place our orders. Many conversations were happening at once. It was hard for me to block out all this noise, read the menu, decide what I wanted to order, listen to what my mom was saying, control my anger, and order my food. In addition, I was supposed to remember to be polite during this process.

I ordered a hot beef sandwich, and when it finally arrived, it wasn't hot any more. I let out a scream of frustration. After all, I had learned that this was a fast way to get my point across, and it was the most effective tool I had. I guess the kitchen heard my angry plea as well. My food was warmed up and returned very promptly. What would have taken the waiter ten minutes to attend to on this busy afternoon took only a couple of minutes.

At this same restaurant on a different outing, I let everyone within earshot know that there was a hair in my food and how disgusted I was by it. That food was promptly taken away and returned to me as well. I had quite the reputation. Yet Mother always treated these outbursts not as an attention-seeking behavior but as "teaching moments."

Mother only left me alone for short periods during that first year of my recovery. On one particular day, it was very hot in our house, the window being our only source of ventilation.

Our neighborhood was full of activity: kids were yelling and screaming, cars were honking, and the next door neighbors had their bass-filled rap music unbearably loud. I was still using my wheelchair at this time, and I had to figure out a way to quiet the noise. The constant beat that a neighborhood in the urban core could be famous for in the summertime and this thumping bass resulted in a strong confusion in my head. I thought closing the windows near this noise would help, but there was no way I could master that feat with only one working arm.

I had to figure something out. I reasoned a bit of classical music could drown out the rap music next door. I arduously wheeled myself over to the stereo, using only one arm and switching wheels to position myself next to the old Magnavox. My family had owned this very stereo since I was a child, and I had spent hours playing with it. Then suddenly, to my amazement, I couldn't figure out how to turn it on.

This was quite a blow to my self-esteem. I thought, *"This can't be true."* Then I panicked, which is the worst thing you can do when you are trying to figure something out. I kept trying, while the noise seemed to be getting louder and louder. The pressure was building, and I did the only thing I knew how to do to let it out. After I hurriedly struggled to wheel myself over to the front door, I opened it, pulled up slowly, then stood up.

I wanted everyone in a block radius to hear, so I took a deep breath, and began with a low-toned, bellowing howl. Then in a very loud burst of energy, it all came out at once—like a wild coyote that had caught its prey and was telling the pack where to come for dinner. "Turn your f_ing music down!" I screamed.

My left side was flinging about, providing quite a display of spastic movement, while my right arm remained tightly clenched to my side. Up and down my left arm went, jerking my whole body like a drunken marionette doll. The entire neighborhood stopped and stared as I struggled to control my left side and continued to scream those words.

Finally I stopped. *There,* I thought, *I let everyone know of my frustration and anger.* Someone in the neighborhood had called the police, and I heard the repetitive screeching of a police siren. *There,* I thought, *those people will get it.* However, the police were not called on the people next door for their music being too loud but on me.

When the policemen arrived at my front door (I use the plural "policemen" because they never travel alone in this neighborhood), my mother had returned home from her errand and was helping me with my "quest-turned-behavior problem." She had classical music playing on the stereo and was attempting to calm me down. And, of course, my plan had been successful—the neighbors had turned down their music. The policemen asked, "What seems to be the problem at this residence?" I chimed in, slurring as if I had had too many Martinis, "Excuse me, officers. It was just my head injury manifesting itself again."

After the police left, Mom began her usual practice of using the moments after my intense displays of frustration to help me reason through how I could have figured out a socially acceptable way to solve the situation or calm my frustration by redirecting my attention. We would brainstorm and laugh together about different possible scenarios.

After this display, the neighbors never again laughed at Mom and me, calling out "Lesbians" when Mom assisted me down the front steps to the car. I now had a reputation in this neighborhood. I heard one small boy pointing me out, "There's that crazy lady."

This wasn't an isolated event of odd behavior either. Some days, I would pace all around the house in a circle—through my kitchen, into my room, the bathroom, through the living area, and then begin the circle again, as I looked for the things I had misplaced that day. This was very time consuming, and I suppose I realized subconsciously that I was probably looking right at the lost item but couldn't recognize it through my fog of panic. There was no relief from my panic. I couldn't relax, sit still or stop my nagging thoughts.

I would continue my ritual of pacing back and forth, pacing through areas I had visited before, flipping through papers, turning over pillows, looking behind the dresser one more time. I would look everywhere, even the trash. This pacing wouldn't stop until someone would assist me, or I would look in the mirror and, feeling foolish, would see my glasses on top of my head. The lost items were usually not hidden, but quite obvious in front of me. I just couldn't see them through my panic. I frequently displayed a sense of frustration, as if I couldn't follow some map to help me hunt down a lost treasure.

This is a poem I wrote on one of those hot days in the summer of 1991:

Low income housing across the street.
Has low mentalities to make money
for the bills they must meet.

Shouting at one another.

Thinking they must be loud
to be understood by the other.

Horns honking with impatience.

Not once. Not twice.

As if their future passenger
is not at all nice.

Children yelling, reacting from the
examples their parents are telling.

Boom, boom, boom,
of several different jams.

These people think it is cool
to be the loudest in all lands.

This is advertisement for free.

There is a thief tuned into the ghetto plan, "only
look out for me."

I'm thankful when it rains or snows.

This is when the yelling goes inside.

Only to store up
like steam in a pot
before it blows.

For now, in the season I most fright.
I have to block out the noises
throughout the night.

I keep earplugs right by my bed.

No one can make earplugs
for the noises inside my head.

~CHAPTER NINE~

Growing Up All Over Again

I had to somehow pay for my existence, and Mom figured out how to go through the process of getting me approved for Social Security Disability Insurance (SSDI). A small monthly payment from the government helped me to regain some of my dignity. I had become financially dependent on my family at twenty-two years-old—ironic, since I had perhaps rushed my independence too soon at seventeen.

The only hint of my past job and tax history was in a tan filing case, which had been rescued from my studio apartment and had survived storage. The responsibility of figuring out my financial past was forced on my mother. A mother's job is never done. She had to put together my mixed up jigsaw puzzle. The pieces were all there, but the person who knew how to put it together was now *part* of this jigsaw puzzle.

At this point, my depression was compounding. I only progressed because Mom insisted that I get out of bed every day, go to therapy, complete exercises, and plan social activities. We trudged forward together through the thick fog of my depression, even though I had to stare at the ground with every step. I had to be sure of proper foot placement and sure that I cleared any obstacles out of the way—and all just to keep my balance.

I was growing up all over again. How to pay for life was too complex of an issue for me to comprehend. This is the very issue that, if someone does not have family to help them with payments, money, or taxes; can cause him to become a ward-of-the-state, dependent on institutionalized living. The treatment at these institutions is exactly equal to your award from the government programs, SSI or SSDI. The money, or monthly award, is used to pay the institution, and you are given a small amount of money for personal items each month from the Independent Living Facility.

Completing the application process and all the required paperwork for my disability claim was not a pleasant task, even for Mom. Though she had earned a Master's degree, she still had difficulty completing this abundance of detailed forms. I wasn't able to be of any assistance at this stage of my development. I was not able to read between the lines, figuratively, or even literally, because of vision difficulties. I stated everything I knew truthfully about any topic, adding everything under the sun. Furthermore, since I had double vision, I had to physically hold a piece of paper, a ruler, or anything I could find that was straight, under each line to allow me to follow along. The paperwork might as well have been printed in a foreign language as far as I was concerned. I later learned that everyone feels that applying for disability is difficult—especially when you are having problems understanding the questions and don't remember the answers.

The reality that I could not process information made my losses seem insurmountable. I had lost my job, my apartment, my car, and my independence, but my most difficult loss encompassed everything: my cognitive abilities. The extent of my losses had begun to become apparent to me.

To get approval for SSDI, I had to attend a session with an assigned psychologist and undergo a series of tests. My mother made certain she was available at the appointment time. The testing site was accessible, near the hospital and on the bus route, but we decided to drive there in one of mom's many jalopy-type cars. I can't remember which one it was this time, but I remember thinking, many times, that the bus might be a more reliable way to get around town. Mostly, however, I just remember the ground. I limped there, staring down at the ground and using Mom as my human cane.

We found the brown building, entered the brown room, and sat down in the brown chairs. The room smelled like dust. The psychologist was busy on the phone as we entered. He guided me to a black industrial-style chair in front of his pristine, industrial-style desk. Mom pulled up a matching chair to sit beside me. She was still in *Mama-Bear* mode. This role was hard for Mother to put back in her case that contained all the different roles she had had to play throughout my recovery.

The testing began, and the questions began flying by. I had difficulty with puzzles, reading, sequencing, comprehension, and writing.

These tests seemed to take a long time to complete, and in the meantime, I had no idea why I was at this brown place in this black chair. I was thinking, "Who does this man think he is to keep asking me all of these stupid questions? I knew all of the answers in kindergarten. Doesn't he know that?"

I did know one thing—this person testing me was making me feel stupid. I couldn't answer the questions fast enough. I wanted to scream at the little man behind the shiny, black desk. He kept changing topics, and each new topic made me feel even smaller. Then he would shoot another question at me. It would sting like a bullet, as I was unable to find the words to answer or even to understand the concepts. I was uncomfortable and confused. Fidgeting in my chair, I wondered why he kept on doing this to me. Then I would look at Mother for the answer to the questions. She was always able to know what word I was searching for, to fill in my gaps during the unusually long passage of time I spent searching. I couldn't understand why she wasn't accepting the usual passing of the baton during this marathon of questions. I figured the man behind the desk must not have known that his barrage was overwhelming me.

He kept firing, and my irritation grew. As the questions lowered my self-esteem, I grew shorter and shorter, slumping over further and further as he kept on. Then, finally, it was over. I felt like Bambi when the huntsmen stopped firing the bullets that killed his mother: confused, wide-eyed, and wondering what had just happened as he shouted "Mother, Mother, help me." I felt like I'd been abandoned all on my own and wondered if the attack would begin again. I suppose you could say that I've watched too many kid shows with my daughters.

Mother didn't recognize the signs that I was becoming frustrated. She was too busy taking notes. She shared with me once we had left the brown building that she was taking notes on which topics gave me trouble, thinking that we would concentrate on these things or that she would suggest them to my therapists.

On our way home, I shared with Mom that I had felt like I just wanted to scream at that man. She replied, "That would have been okay to scream. After all, the psychologist was trained to diffuse such anger outbursts. Besides, if you had screamed, that would have been a good display of your everyday behavior." I never screamed for that psychologist, but there were many more opportunities to come, for me to display my now-famous screaming.

Later on, Mom talked with me about the dichotomy that the SSDI application process presents. She explained to me that I was in the midst of trying to find out who I had become as a newly disabled person; I was recovering physically as well as coping with losing my independence as an adult. I was struggling to stay positive and focus on what I could do, while the SSDI application process was forcing me to focus on and list my disabilities. She helped me realize why the system focuses on the many life skills that a person has lost and their inability to perform the daily tasks necessary for independence. A person should always remember to report how they perform tasks on their worst day, and not their best. Mother was trying to help me refocus my train of thought, and it was her idea to focus on my abilities, not my *dis*-abilities. Social Security requires a person to do just the opposite if she wants to get the documentation necessary to receive aide.

Psychologists, whether employed by SSDI or in private practice, are forced to document their sessions using medical jargon for reasons of legality, and this is generally not intended for the patient to read. A psychologist employed by Social Security could have reported in their terminology the following, for example: "Applicant presents slow response time, depressed mood, appears uncomfortable, not using walking device, walking with significant right quadrant semi-paresis, scoring four out of five of criteria, possesses inability to perform necessary daily-life activities independently." This is only an example of the mindset of the medical model that Social Security is forced to adhere to, not a real document.

People who have experienced a TBI have a tendency to stay in the medical model and experience difficulty when they are medically stable and could evolve into the next step, eventually living independently. The question should be explored of why TBI survivors vacillate between living on their own or in a facility?

The medical model plays an important role in helping to sustain the life of the patient when they are in a comatose state and are in physical need of primary care in an institution. Expensive tests are performed throughout the patient's hospital stay until they are determined stabilized. Even after they are determined medically stable, the TBI patient is recognized as having a medical problem.

I was at the point where I had to deal with my losses to go forward, and not do as Social Security implies you should do in their barrage of questions: stay stagnant as you realize the large number of actions you are unable to perform. Now I realize that Mom just wanted me to have the opportunity to become self-sufficient, to work hard toward becoming all that I was able to become; not concentrating on what I couldn't change but changing what I could. She realized that rehabilitation could only take me so far physically. I had to do all the hard work emotionally. I believe she wanted to help me realize that I could change the things that would make my life meaningful again to me.

It is my opinion that I could have been diagnosed with several different psychotic illnesses throughout my recovery. Several situations occur to me that could have alarmed my mother, causing her to seek psychiatric services for me.

This could have had a dramatic affect on my prognosis. A psychiatrist not educated in brain injury could have directed me to hospitalization for obsessive-compulsive disorder at one point, schizophrenia with psychotic features for a short period of time, and Bipolar Disorder, or aggressive behaviors with explosive criteria, for another brief period. This would have caused a downward spiral of misdiagnosis and improper use of psychotropic medication, which would have or could have caused me to believe I was insane. These features might then have caused me to believe I was having a mental health crisis.

Similar to the "Placebo Effect," I probably would have believed that because my "inappropriate behaviors" were improving that it must be the medication that was responsible and not my own brain's masked healing efforts. My brain was just going through stages of making sense out of everything. I would have always believed, "Well they are the doctors. They must be right."

The depression brought on by the large number of friendships that abruptly ended after my accident could have started the cycle of over-medication, causing confusion in an already confused mind, followed by attempts to overdose, hospitalization, evaluation of medications, a new diagnosis or two, then new medications, causing more over-medication in a healing mind, then on and on.

The individual who experiences a brain injury doesn't have to listen to a doctor who thinks they have reached their final plateau and will not make any more progress after the magical "six-month period" as many suggest. When recognized and treated like a temporary state of the healing process, the family or staff are more willing to see a person through a year, or perhaps longer, of inappropriate outbursts of anger, realizing that healing is happening. The healing in an unmedicated brain can progress and continue to amaze persons convinced that medication is the best treatment for brain injury.

Staff or family willing to go through these tough times need to realize that the brain must make new connections to process thoughts, and that this takes time. The injured brain has to go through some difficult stages of learning what is and is not appropriate, through therapy, and have family or staff in place who can help in the healing process. Caregivers can assist by providing the stability that comes from a consistent relationship with the same caregivers, who all work with the same goal in mind for the TBI survivor. The caregivers must be educated in rehabilitation and realize that the person with whom they are working has had their world jumbled from brain injury.

Families can recognize that their loved one is slowly emerging from the cocoon in which head injury has wrapped them.

Knowing this, they can celebrate the metamorphosis into this new person—a person different from what he was before the head injury. They may see small increments of change for the better, in the placement of a foot as he struggles to walk, for example, or perhaps in communicating at a more appropriate speed or not being confused in conversation.

Slowly a life is emerging and a homeostasis can begin. This may be a slow progression of events, but the dedicated will receive all the recognition as the survivor is finally able to figure out her checkbook on her own.

~CHAPTER TEN~

Accepting Who I've Become

While living at my mother's home, I went to outpatient therapy as long as my insurance would pay for it. The insurance coverage lasted about six months after my hospitalization. Then my coverage topped out. I went through the appropriate discharge plans and was set loose to do the exercises on my own at home. I had to independently perform exercises such as stretching my arm to the point of pain and beyond, or picking up checkers or other similarly-sized objects to practice fine motor skills with my partially paralyzed right hand. *Yeah right, I'll get right to it.* I would think to myself as they were giving me instructions on how I could do the exercising by myself at home on my own. I remember thinking as they were happily dismissing me, *Oh, sure. I'll do it. Not gonna happen.*

This made me feel as if all my treatment and care were dependent on the amount of money that I or my family had in assets—on whether we had prepared for a disabling experience and could pay for the luxury of therapy in an out-patient suite. I daydream about the possibility of being wealthy, the possibility that given enough money, I could be free of my overt signs of having brain damage, or perhaps that I would have more use of my right arm that tightly gripped my right side as if protecting my ribs.

But the reality was to expect me to do the prescribed exercises all on my own. Daily, I was expected to recreate this frustrating torture through holding up the newspaper, cooking, folding clothes, putting up my own hair, all using my hand that was barely receiving signals from my brain. My hand only received very faint signals, like those received by a distant ship that can hardly hear the fog horn at the lighthouse telling it to move out of danger.

I knew what I *could* do. I *could* separate my middle finger from the tightly gripped fist of my hand. As I struggled to keep my arm and hand up, I could slowly and with much effort will the middle finger to independently appear. The phrase that normally follows such a gesture need not be uttered; it was such an arduous task that it became apparent what I was trying to communicate.

I wish I could be the perfectly rehabilitated individual and say, "I diligently stuck to my daily routine of exercises." Isn't that what a person who has successfully recovered to their fullest capacity claims? What is fullest capacity? Is there a rule or a boundary in raising children to achieve their fullest personal capacity? What is this definition? I say, *choose your battles.* Each person on this earth has a different definition for fullest capacity, and I had to redefine mine. I don't see what's wrong with living with a disability. I could no longer afford therapy, especially if being a patient was to be for the rest of my life.

My rehabilitation physician told me, "Life will be your therapy at this point." I will have this injury the entirety of my adulthood, traditional therapy had reached a plateau, and now it was up to me to choose my battles and figure out a way to work these exercises into my life.

I could have overwhelmed myself, concentrating all my efforts on my physical ailment and my reasoning/cognitive skills at the same time. There were so many things wrong with me physically that I put my effort into what I knew I could change through repetition. If I overwhelmed myself then there would be the fear of failure; I could end up just giving up on all of it. As it is, I am an eligible candidate for therapy of some kind for the rest of my life.

The fact that I was motivated to do the daily exercises was a key ingredient needed to achieve and succeed in my goal plan. The plan was to work on my cognitive skills and speech, hoping that my physical and fine motor movements wouldn't fall too far behind. After all, you can get through life without raising your arm above your head, but you can't get through life without using your head.

Next, I faced the necessity of acknowledging my changed self—a self with different abilities—and accepting the transformation. All of the wishing and praying to be miraculously returned to the "Old Becky" was futile. I also had to help my friends and family understand this as well. My life and my brain had been changed forever. I will never be the same person. Accepting the new world I had been forced to confront and not looking back were my challenges.

This is not what every person who rehabilitates after a TBI must do, but concentrating on returning to the person I was before would have been a waste of my energy. I would never return to modeling; I could barely walk. I would never cocktail waitress again; I couldn't carry a tray and walk at the same time or remember the orders. I wasn't interested in returning as a travel agent. My life before my accident seemed so shallow and superficial. I had to create a new life with new interests.

This didn't happen in a day, in months, or even in years. In fact, it will continue to evolve till the day I die. I realize now that I would not have matured past that stage of development if everyone had expected me to be the person I was before. I had to realize and redefine my existence.

My sister Debbie said, "They told me that she would never be the 'Becky' that I once knew. I refused to believe it. I think that this was the hardest thing for me to realize. She was my best friend, my sister. Becky and I are five years apart, but very close. She was a free spirit, and I was a bit more conservative. She made people feel good when they were around her. She had an energy that was indescribable. She was a star. When she walked in a room, the place would light up, and the party would begin. Becky was a great dancer too, very sexy, and guys' mouths would drop open when they saw her. She is still gorgeous."

I began volunteer work to fill my empty time. My skewed vision and slow walking and speech delayed my progress. I contacted a church down the street and was asked to serve food at a soup kitchen. Well, I didn't exactly serve the food, due to my limited coordination. I was designated as the official greeter to direct the line of participants. This was a perfect job for me because I can talk to anyone. I volunteered in the summer before school started.

One bright and sunny evening for dinner, I showed up for my daily volunteer job dressed in a loose-fitting, thinly woven cloth summer dress and sandals. I recognized a few people from the bus line and greeted them with a healthy, "Well, hello there!" The line had backed up. It was not moving, and there were several people waiting. I decided to adjust my sandal, and I innocently bent down at the waist. There was an older, gray-haired man standing before me, waiting for the line to move forward. He was at just the right angle to see my entire exposed chest.

He looked me straight in the eyes and calmly said, "That was beautiful. Thank you. You made my day." I reflect on all of the comments that such an action could have caused, and how this man politely and graciously thanked me for my unintentional, unique form of greeting.

My volunteering at a soup kitchen was a moment in my life that would not have happened had I not been transformed on that June day in 1989. Before that, I was too self-absorbed and egocentric to consider other people's unfortunate circumstances. I now had a second chance to grow up with my mom in the city, instead of moving away to live with my dad as I had done when I was twelve. In my attempt to grow up in my adolescent years without my mother's guidance, I had turned into what other people had expected of me instead of what I wanted to be.

December 1970, Sharon with (L to R) Debbie, Nancy, and Becky in Marshall, MO.

Greetings...
FROM OUR HOME TO YOURS!

(L to R) Becky, Sammie, Nancy, Debbie

SAM, SHARON, SAMMIE
DEBORAH, NANCY AND REBEKAH

~CHAPTER ELEVEN~

Family Two Ways (To Go)

My mom took a courageous step when she divorced my father and moved us out of the small town. She moved me and my three siblings from Marshall, Missouri to Kansas City, Missouri; around 100 miles west. My family was constantly changing in composition, as my siblings moved back-and-fourth from my mom's to my dad's, and as an additional person occasionally came to live with us, chipping in to pay rent, or possibly sleeping with my mother, in a variety of relationships.

I just followed along: never asking questions, constantly gaining skills and adapting to new environments in different schools, always being "the new kid." My assumption, when I grew older, was that moving was Mom's self-therapy for the deep bouts of depression she would experience: this shifting around would shake up our problems, and the end result of all this jumbling, the changing addresses and phone numbers, was that all our problems would be left behind never to find us again.

Mom was depressed and frustrated over the low pay that being an Art teacher earned her; this, combined with the need to obtain a Master's degree, and having to live without much assistance from my father for the four (sometimes three) of us was often discouraging. Dad did graciously pay a sum of $250.00 on time each month, but it barely contributed to our cost-of-living.

My father provided stability. He owned his own business *Dyer the Flyer, Inc.* He was a pilot, a flight instructor, and also an auctioneer at estate sales and the like. He was considered wealthy in this town of 12,000. He lived a comfortable life with his new family, who blended at quite a fast pace with ours. I had felt as if I had been forgotten about as he cared for my new step-mother Mary, and two new children. Staci (a girl my age) became my new stepsister and John (four years younger than me) my new step-brother. Seven years later, my dad had another child with his new wife, Matt who was my half-brother.

Then there were the four Dyer siblings, who went into the mix. There was Sam (six years older than me), Debbie (five years older), then, born exactly three years before me, my sister Nancy. Mother reports, "Just after singing "Happy Birthday" to Nancy, I called the doctor, headed to the hospital, and pushed Rebekah out." Nancy says, "You ruined my birthday party."

Twelve years later, Mom was surprised with another girl, Sarah. Sarah made March 11th, the day that Nancy and I shared, even more special. Now there were three of us on the same day. This made the day a miracle, Guiness Book of World Records material, you would think. Especially since these are three girls born on the same day in three different years, one even having a different father. I believe that recorded births on the same day have usually involved fertility drugs and twins.

We Dyer siblings lived happily, bouncing between the two homes; though, unfortunately, often in poverty. Mom went to graduate school, while she worked as an Art instructor *and* a waitress to tirelessly provide for her family. Meanwhile, only a hundred miles to the east, my stepfamily lived in Marshall with a full refrigerator and a controlled environment: heat in the winter and air conditioning in the summer. Air conditioning would have been a luxury for me growing up in my mother's house. In the wintertime, we worried monthly about whether to keep the phone on or heat the house. We couldn't even consider air conditioning. I sometimes visited Marshall during the holidays; it was only then that I could forget for a while about the problems of living in the city.

Mother did not have much money, but she provided a rich life for us in another sense: rich in a appreciation for the Arts, and rich in opportunities to confront life's difficult lessons with the strength and support that comes from being part of a close family.

Part of our closeness, grew from the summer-long vacations we spent together in our VW van, often camping in the mountains of Colorado. Mom would load us all up for many a road trip, and we would eat and sleep in our van until we arrived at our destination. Through all of the unexpected problems life threw at us, Mom taught decision-making skills that flowed from her wealth of experience, *and* she instilled in each of us the love that would be our guide in making our own decisions.

Although Dad provided a comfortable environment where we didn't have to worry about how the bills would be paid, it lacked hugs of appreciation, gratitude, and love. I came to appreciate the summer-long vacations in Mom's VW van, put up with our moving, and never gave into leading the sheltered life with Dad. I stayed with Mom until the eighth grade.

Mom talked openly with me on Christmas break that year, as she and her new boyfriend drove me and my belongings down to my father's, where I would live while attending high school. She told me she felt she'd laid a solid foundation in an effort to prevent me from developing a small town mentality.

I graduated high school in January of my senior year and immediately moved back to Kansas City. At the tender age of 17, I set out on my own, staying briefly with an older sister, her husband, and their young son, as I worked to save money. Then, as soon as I turned 18 and could rent an apartment, I was off and running.

By 1989, at the age of 22, I had fully claimed my independence as an adult. I was working as a professional model, a travel agent, and a cocktail waitress. Yet I still felt I was struggling to make sense of my place in the world. As I drove home following an argument with my boyfriend, I was wrestling with my thoughts when my complicated world was abruptly shut off. I knew the intersection well, having walked past it for two years on my way to grade school. I pulled my car away from the stop sign; then as I merged onto the two-way street, a speeding car struck mine and my world went dark.

On a Thanksgiving holiday only eighteen months post-injury, I returned to visit my father's home in Marshall. My stepmother always polished up her silver and put on a big production to celebrate this holiday. It was a huge family gathering with all of my father's family from his second marriage in attendance. This part of my extended family had not yet had the opportunity to get to know me very well since my injury. Even though the house where we gathered had been built in preparation for my birth in 1967, I was unable to recall many memories of my life there.

Now, a year and a half post-injury, I tried to avoid drawing any attention to myself. I was feeling uncomfortable about my slow speech; on top of which, I had huge chunks of misplaced memories. My memories seemed to me like a television channel that I could not easily tune in. To receive my memories, I had to strategically position my rabbit ears and stand at just the right spot, extending my arms awkwardly; only then did the pictures become clear.

In other words, the memories were there and could be prompted, but it took some time—more time than normal conversation allowed. There was a silent, uncomfortable pause as I would wait for the process working so hard in my brain to deliver the appropriate words or memories. Imagined I could feel the neurons shooting out their feelers, branch-like dendrites, seeking other neurons with the right information. They traveled through the scar tissue, depending on the lesser damaged right side of my brain to work overtime.

At this dinner, there were at least five conversations going on at once with this happy bunch of family. I thought, *they seem to know everything about me.* All I could do was look at them, as my brain hurriedly went through files, thinking, *what are their names?* My brain could have started a fire from all of the lightening bolts shooting out signals in my brain as they looked for the information! *Name, name, dummy you forgot their names.*

After everyone had gathered around the table, and I had clumsily filled my plate, surviving several near-misses as I managed to keep turkey and dressing on my plate and off the floor, I thought *now I can relax.* Then a question was asked. All at once, every eye was on me and every conversation stopped. Speaking to me in a manner that implied I had problems understanding and would not be able to respond, someone asked, "When are you going to start school at the community college?" I found the looks of doubt especially humiliating.

I responded with confidence, "I fart in the stall." I was intending to proudly comment that I would start in the fall. I expected laughter and joking to burst the slow bubble of words that had taken shape, but no one laughed. This should have been a time of laughter to ease the tension I was feeling. My acquired family had always had a good time laughing at each of our quirks or faults. Now I just assumed that they felt pity for me, and they didn't want to hurt my feelings by laughing at my response. Everyone returned to their conversations and the subject was dropped.

During my formative adolescent years, I should have been able to grow up asking my mother questions, bouncing jokes and ideas about my future off her. Instead, I had spent them in this small town.

At twenty-two, I learned from my mom how to be kind, down-to-earth, genuinely trusting, and open to another's experience without judgment. The fact that I thought I was twelve when I began realizing I had been in a coma for the entire summer is significant. It was around that time when Mother and I had left off ten years earlier. I finally got to bounce ideas off my mother. I would have never gone to college if it had not been for my mom's guidance and unwavering support. She was my real case manager.

Dyer family, Easter 1980

Top Row, L to R: Debbie (sister), John Makings (stepbrother), Becky, Sam, Jr. (brother), Nancy (sister), Debby Riely (family friend who lived with us), Stacie Makings (stepsister) *Seated:* Sam, Sr. (father), Mary (stepmother), Matthew (half-brother) in the home at Marshall, MO

~CHAPTER TWELVE~

Who Becky Was

In the last two years at the "Eiker House," I finally became confident in walking up and down stairs. On the top floor of my mom's home was a third floor apartment. My sister Nancy began helping me fix it up, starting with painting the kitchen. I remember hurting Nancy's feelings unintentionally one afternoon through my social illness of excessively telling the truth.

She was up on a ladder, working hard to help me create a habitable environment. It was hot in the kitchen that day. We had a big window open, the one that frequently let opossums crawl in from the huge oak tree. The aging oak tree stretched its branches over mom's three-story, white-pillared, Victorian-style house.

The wind blew in through the kitchen window after skimming over what was probably the original black tar roof that over-looked the huge front porch. This hot breeze was beginning to get to us, as we tried to create a kitchen out of what had once been used for just storage. I felt guilty about my inability to climb a ladder and help out as Nancy kept scraping off old wall paper preparing to paint.

She was wearing a pair of jeans that I had given her from the stockpile of clothing returned to me. I said, "Those are tight on you, do you want me to take them back?" That was the last I saw of Nancy for a while. She stomped right out of that kitchen and didn't come back for a week.

This reaction began to teach me how brutal honesty wasn't always the best route to take. Nancy later told mom, "I didn't look forward to visiting you and Becky at this time, because you won't lie and Becky can't."

Mother would never lie to you just to make a situation more comfortable. She was up front and honest—sometimes painfully honest, but this characteristic could also be a strength. It certainly made her the perfect case manager for me. She would, for example, tell me outright when I was repeating a story, gently saying, "I know you told me that before."

There have been many situations where I wasn't told that I was repeating myself. It seems people would just quietly listen. This left me wondering, *Am I repeating myself?* I have taken a different stance on life now. I think life is too short to care about such frivolity. I should feel fortunate that I'm alive. People will think what they will, and it is not up to me to decide how they feel about me.

These may seem like simple adolescent concepts, but these were ideas that the Becky I was before the accident just wouldn't have accepted. Becky had to make sure that everyone liked her, and if they didn't, she would make certain they would. Everyone had to be brought around to her way of thinking.

I realize now that I've experienced a brush with death, how each person has their own set of ideas they've developed through personal growth. This is why I consider Becky to have been shallow or just on the surface. Perhaps this is one of those personality traits that a person grows out of as they get older. Becky was a young lady who had been independent for only five years and therefore had limited experience in the matters of life that really count; for example, buying a home, choosing a life partner, or gaining education towards a career.

After my life was almost taken away, I finally *got* it. I came to believe that people don't just acquire a positive attitude, but have experiences that teach them how to live life from the inside. By this, I mean living a positive life for yourself, based on your own ideals, not based on what others think you should be or do.

Becky left her personal growth by the wayside when she chose to reflect what everyone else wanted from her. Everyone would comment that she should be a model, so she became one. Who knows where I would be today if my life had continued to merely reflect what other people wanted from me? I am past wondering now and have grown to be content.

If no one is able to take away anything else from this memoir, I will be happy if the reader realizes this simple concept that I have found to be of the utmost importance: you need to live your own life for yourself. Can you answer the question, "if my life were to end tomorrow, what would really matter?"

Part of my answer came in deciding to further my education, and part of that meant figuring out reasonable transportation to and from the inner-city community college. I walked, or I should say *limped,* dragging my right extremities and wearing a huge backpack, two blocks to a bus stop, then I transferred to another bus at a busy intersection, and finally to complete the journey, I walked a block through a huge parking lot to the college campus everyday.

I have always completed everything that I set out to do, school was no exception. I was determined to stay focused and finish what I had started. I went to school Monday through Friday, and like therapy, I treated my education as employment. Regardless of whether I had class, study lab, or study group plans on campus, I still took my journey, keeping the routine. I needed a considerable amount of knowledge to find my classes and figure out a schedule that would work to make my college experience less stressful. I knew I didn't think so well when I felt stressed.

In the fall of 1990, I began by enrolling in a non-credit course at the community college. I started slowly because I knew that if I took on too much right away I would surely cause myself frustration, resulting in failure. I started by taking admission tests, then took more tests to find out my interests. I took one class at first, then two, then three, slowly increasing my course load. Finally, I began to realize what I could do and stopped concentrating on what I couldn't.

In other words, find your strengths and steer your future accordingly. I took advantage of every service there was at the school to help a person with a disability succeed. It was difficult to acknowledge that I even had a "disability." At one point, I wanted all the disability signs for parking to be renamed "unique ability." There was no "dis" in my personal description. I just found unique ways to get things accomplished.

There are a number of people who have a *dis*-ability of some sort with its own unique set of circumstances. They may be struggling with dyslexia or any number of learning difficulties. They may be struggling with an unstable home environment that makes succeeding in college difficult. They may lack the self-confidence it requires to do well in college. Whatever the circumstances, we're all in this together. Explore the opportunities offered at the school, and don't be ashamed to take advantage of any free programs.

I slowly improved as I took small course loads, and arranged my classes with lots of time in between to get from point A to point B—both physically and mentally. It was difficult for me to change my concentration from one subject to the next, and, as is required by society, to multi-task at a fast pace throughout the day.

I used many techniques to help me succeed. I took exams in a quiet environment with extended time. I asked a person in class who could write fast to take notes for me. I tape recorded each class, took what notes I could myself, and spent hours poring over the material. Daily, I would listen to the lecture on tape (utilizing my auditory memory), read the notes taken for me (visual memory), fill in the gaps in my personal notes (written or kinesthetic memory), and repeat this sequence until an exam. My short-term memory deficit, distorted vision, and inability to block out noises were my biggest challenges. Learning memorization strategies, reading assignments at least twice by closing one eye or holding the text at a certain angle, and using earplugs to block out all the noises in my environment, all led me to my first degree. I graduated a two-year program in three years by going twelve months a year.

Just getting to a destination was quite an exhausting experience. I always gave myself plenty of time to rest. I met quite a few interesting characters on the bus line in the process. One day, a man using inner-city slang asked me, "You on the job market, girl?" I must have asked him to repeat his question three times, due to my difficulty understanding him and my inability to translate. Possibly he was drunk that morning, making it difficult for me to interpret all the words slurred together as they were, with such slang and insult to the English language.

There were several people on the bus daily that appeared drunk. This never bothered me because I appeared drunk as well. Daily on the bus, all the people would just look at each other, bouncing up and down, sometimes talking. I wondered about each of our different circumstances, each of us pulling the alert string to stop at the same bus stop each day, putting an end to our daily "Metro bus party time" together.

It was difficult for me to conceal my feelings, even though sometimes showing them might have unfortunate consequences—especially then, in fact, because of how intense my emotions could be at such times; like when I found myself in the wrong place without somebody or something to back me up, or help me reason my way through the dangers; or like when a stranger would intentionally cause me anger. I had a hard time ignoring such behavior and not getting angry with them.

Many situations like these occurred while I was a disabled guest at my daily "Metro Parties." Some could have escalated and even become horribly dangerous had I responded out of the "quick-to-react" mentality I possessed at this stage of recovery. There were several instances when people would intentionally wink or whisper "psst, hey baby." This rude behavior would cease when they saw my difficulty walking.

On one particular day, I wasn't on my familiar route on the inner-city bus system. My sister, now twelve, and I were off to do a cool summertime activity and wanting to save a 2-mile walk, we decided to hop on the bus. We were going to cool off in the pool at the local YMCA.

As we walked to our bus stop there were unattended children jumping on a stack of old mattresses, which had been waiting to be hauled off to the landfill. (At least, I think they were unattended. Maybe they were attended and their parents just didn't see this as a particularly dangerous or hazardous activity.) They had imaginatively turned a couple of full-size mattresses so they were stacked onto each other as if they were their professional trampoline. What I witnessed could have been children competing for a gold medal in gymnastics. The flips were magnificently high with many somersaults turned in the air, then each child completed his routine with a timely dismount for the next child to attempt his.

Car stereos were all blasting out their bass-filled music, interspersed with moments of unusual quiet. Then a blast of sound would make up for it, perfecting the ghetto symphony. We had only two blocks to walk until we reached the spot where we sat to wait for the bus.

The women keeping us company at this bus stop were dressed in bright, shiny clothes. The outfits the women wore were not at all appropriate for the weather or the temperature on the thermometer. They were obviously trying to raise temperatures of a different kind. My little sister and I didn't fit in. Obviously, we hadn't been filled in on the dress code for this corner on a hot summer day as we innocently waited to go to the pool. I felt uncomfortable being there with several six-foot-one women who stood proudly with their bright red lips and stiletto heels waiting for their next trick.

Cars flew by us, swishing our hair as each swerved by the busy corner. Finally the huge public bus arrived, blowing a blast of hot air out of its tail pipe as it pulled up by the curb. Then the doors flew open and out came a bubble of cool air to refresh us.

It was rush hour for this bus, and there wasn't a seat to be found. I stumbled as the bus took off before all the passengers were seated. I stumbled again attempting to find an area to hold on to. I fell backward, then forward, completely controlled by the inertia of every turn the bus made. People just kept getting on and getting off, confusing me too much to see any opportunities to sit down. I accidentally stepped on a woman's foot in my quest to stabilize my badly off-balance posture. I thought she was going to hit me in retaliation for my clumsiness.

Rosa Parks would have been ashamed of this lady's behavior. All of these young ladies were watching my difficulty in keeping myself up off of the floor, and just staring and laughing at me, refusing to help out. One skinny lady said, "Hey ger, you stay off my feet." As if I would intentionally step on her foot.

I'm sure Rosa Parks would have given up her seat for a woman with a disability. But these women were just rubbing it into my pale face, laughing at my imperfections, pleased that they had a seat and I didn't.

I spoke in a shaky upset tone, "Oh, excuse me, for I stepped on someone's dainty foot as if I might need some help."

I gave the smart-alecky girl a look that was so angry that she didn't say another word. I think she would have defended her territory, but she sensed I was about to blow. I stared at the ground until she and her friends got off at the next stop, giggling under their breath. I refused to give one of them any eye contact.

It took me quite a while to cool off from this adventure, an adventure that had itself started out in search of coolness. But Mom turned it around like she always did by using it as a teaching moment.

Mom asked me what I had been feeling on the bus and helped me to recognize my hot face and tingling hands as signs I was becoming angry. She taught me that when I felt like I was so mad that I just wanted to hit someone, I could stop my thought process by focusing on something more positive—sort of like changing the subject when someone is whining on and on about how bad things are. I could do the same thing in my own brain. I could stop the feedback loop and even help my anger dissipate by finding some humor in the situation.

Concentrating on angry feelings just made me more and more angry. By not concentrating on the anger, I found that I could deny it the opportunity to keep growing bigger and bigger until it overwhelmed me and came out in one of my famous outbursts. I learned a lot from this bad experience, and I slowly began to realize that I was now in control of my own emotions.

Mom had a lot of experience of her own at riding the bus. She befriended many of the street people she met on the bus as she talked to them about their struggle to survive.

I cannot remember a time when she wasn't this way. Mom has always been sensitive to the disenfranchised population and an expert at finding the good in anyone.

One of those she befriended was a man who frequented the inner-city area that I traveled. He took notice when I would transfer between buses by taking a shortcut through an alley way. He knew a lot from walking the streets and observing the crowds, so when he saw my mother at a local coffee shop, he stopped in to give her a piece of advice about me.

"Tell your daughter not to walk through that alley anymore," he cautioned. "Squatters are back there and could get her to cash in on their next hit." My mother alerted me to this danger, and I listened carefully.

I was so tired of taking the bus, but knowing the bus system did give me a sense of independence. I could get anywhere in the city on it and frequently did. There were a few times that people would recognize me resting in a bus shelter and offer me a ride to my destination. Strangers offered me a ride at least every other day. I accepted only twice in all those times. I had become very street-smart, but I suppose my mom would have frowned on any exceptions to "never accept rides from strangers." I can just hear the speech I would get.

I had a sense about the two people that I did accept rides from. One was a student and understood my struggle with my heavy backpack. The other man seemed sincere, saying, "I have had a stroke and experienced not being able to walk and sore feet." In retrospect, I suppose this could have been a lie to coax me into his car, but I sensed his honesty. I met a lot of nice people in my local transit experience.

I remember sitting at a bus stop once waiting for a bus that was late. As I watched the cars go by with just one person in each vehicle, it occurred to me how selfish and what a glutton the average American was with his huge gas-guzzling car. The average American couldn't be inconvenienced by carpooling or using the bus system to help clean our environment. This new global sense had certainly not been part of Becky. She only looked at *herself* in the rearview mirror and not at all the people behind her driving on the same highway.

The time came when I had to accept that the crowd of people I chose to spend my time with had changed drastically as well. My sister Nancy has given me a sour taste of what my interests were before that transforming summer. In reply to my questionnaire, she wrote, "My sister Becky had the desire to gather up material things such as clothes, money, a sharp-looking car, jewelry, shoes, fancy leather jackets, furs, as well as a multitude of other expensive things."

I am no longer interested in this lifestyle. Since my reorganization after TBI, I realize that this type of lifestyle is as cold as the people it attracts. Learning that I was this type of person seems foreign to me because I don't think that way any longer. This type of person doesn't have time to care about his fellow man who struggles day-to-day to survive, shivering at the bus stop, asking for quarters to buy the liquor that keeps him warm and settles the shakes from his addiction.

The friends that I had before my accident didn't seem to care about me afterwards. Sure they were interested at first, but you have to understand that the only way these friends knew how to relate to each other was through sort of a "party atmosphere" and any further contact with me and my injuries would surely have dragged them down and spoiled their "party." They were interested in looking good and getting ahead; they didn't have the time to care about what had happened to me.

They certainly didn't stay by me through my difficult times, the period when I wasn't fun to be around and didn't attract the spotlight with my charm and charisma. As a result, my social life had to reinvent itself.

I guess I did have a few friends who endured this detour with me. Tina Maicher was one of them. Tina responded to my questionnaire by saying, "I've known Becky since she first moved to Marshall, MO. She and I worked together the summer before her freshman year in high school. We have spent a lot of time joking, crying, and laughing together. There have been long periods of time when life would pull us away from each other. The funny thing is that it felt like we had never missed a beat once we found each other again. We could pick up right up where we have left off from one another's life.

Becky stood up with me as a bridesmaid in my marriage with Mike; a man we both went to high school with. Her boyfriend in high school was Mike's best friend. Needless to say, just about every day back in the 1980's, we saw one another often in this small town. I was there for her and she was there for me throughout all our turmoil in life.

I remember the day I received the call that she was in the hospital and might not survive. I collapsed in tears unable to compose myself. I think it was her dad, Sam, that called me with the news. That was a time in our lives that I hope we will never have to re-live again. I remember taking trips with Sam up to the city to see Becky at the hospital.

Sam wasn't very good at driving in the city. I guess that is why he chose to be a pilot. It seems to me, and Becky has commented, that he is better off staying up in the air navigating a plane, rather than the stop and go of a vehicle in city driving situations. I remember each trip we went to the hospital to visit Becky, and it wasn't because of the entertaining conversations Sam and I held while traveling. He is a man of few words. I can't imagine how he felt coming close to losing his daughter, as he stared at the road while we traveled the 100 mile journey together. He didn't offer many clues I could go on, to read his feelings. I know what my feeling was; I felt like I had lost a very close friend. She wasn't able start up conversations any more, she wasn't laughing with me, she couldn't cry with me, but she survived. She was alive, but her personality had changed.

Tina and Becky, high school age at Tina's house

There was about a year-long lapse of time before I saw her again. She had changed a lot. During that time I went through a lot of changes myself, and ended up moving not too far away from where she lived with her mom. I didn't know my way around Kansas City that well at first, spent the majority of my time working, so I didn't know how or where she was for a long time.

As she has changed, I too have changed. Maybe not in the same manner or circumstances, but everyone grows and changes from who they were in high school. Becky's changes happened suddenly, not to mention tragically and drastically. Who knows where we would be had this not happened to her? I can say with confidence that we would have still continued our friendship, no matter where we both ended up. I don't like thinking about this phase in our lives. I look forward not back. Looking back hurts too much. Why spend your time hurting? Life is too short.

Becky and I have both changed a lot throughout all of these years. She will always be Beck to me. Nothing can happen that could make me think and feel differently about her. We have a bond that few people ever get to experience. I'm thankful that she pulled through and decided to stay here with us. Now, we all are able to make new memories together."

After Mom received the warning from the homeless man, I decided that something had to change in my routine of getting to school before my "Metro partying days" became too dangerous, and besides, I knew that driving again would make my life easier for me.

I began to go through the process of getting my driver's license reinstated. For insurance reasons, after a person has been in a coma, it is suggested that they be enrolled in a driver's evaluation process and retake the driver's exam to have their license to drive reissued.

I had to be approved through Vocational Rehabilitation for them to assist me with this cost. First, I had to take a test to evaluate my deficits. Yes, another test that showed me how I couldn't do something because of my head injury. No doubt this frustrated me, and I wanted to scream, but I had learned to hold it in until I was in a safe place. Then I could let it out. Hopefully I didn't frighten any unintentional bystanders!

I knew that I could drive. It was just another matter of having to prove my ability with authority questioning me because of my "dis"ability. Mom let me prove my ability to drive while we were on a Sunday drive to my grandmother's house in the country. My older sister thought I was incapable. She got out of the car and walked the remaining three miles to her home—in high-heeled boots, I might add. Nancy thought that my mom had blind belief in my ability. I had to prove my "re"ability to everyone, except for Mom. She believed in me all the way, and when she was doubtful, she helped me reason though the consequences.

I drove depending just on my left side because my right was too slow in reacting. The institution that rehabilitates adults to perform adultlike activities assigned me to an instructor. This instructor took me in a white, plainly marked "student driver" car through the streets and on the highway, constantly testing me to evaluate my thought processes and physical abilities. Everything checked out okay, and I passed all exams allowing me to be an adult member of society again.

My dad passed down an old family car to me, and I was on my way to prove to the world that Rebekah was back from the dead.

~CHAPTER THIRTEEN~

Look What I Can Do, Mom!

I chose to study speech pathology at the beginning of my college career because of the impact that relearning how to speak clearly had on my life. When I was unable to talk clearly, other people would disregard any input I had into a conversation. Sometimes people would even speak loudly to me as if I couldn't understand or hear them. I would hardly ever leave phone messages because of how badly I slurred, not to mention my trouble finding words. When I was with my mom and a person had a question about me, they would talk to me through my mother. They would ask, "How is she doing?" and look at her for a response.

Throughout my time in the hospital and outpatient therapies, I placed an extra emphasis on concentrating hard in speech therapy, slowing down my thoughts so that my mouth could catch up. After about two years, my slurring became obvious only when I was tired. I wanted to help people achieve the gift of speech that had been returned to me, but it soon became obvious to me that this was such a narrow field to impact a person's life, and the course of study seemed to stretch on and on. I had already spent three years getting a two-year degree, and speech pathology was a six-year program.

The speech pathology classes had such a competitive atmosphere. I would have to race to class to get a good seat. I needed to be close to the front so that the lecture could be properly recorded, and I wasn't quick or pushy like my classmates who just wanted to sit in the front row to make a good impression. I spent one year in speech pathology. I felt like I would never get done with school and also felt I was a failure for not completing a goal.

Changing my major to social work was a difficult choice to make, and the Office of Disability Services was instrumental in my decision. I needed to find a major that wasn't dependent on such left-brained activity. This was a difficult step for me. I had to acknowledge that speech pathology wasn't the best major for me. The director of Disability Services listened to me, helped me see my strengths and my natural ability and how to use them to further my desire to assist others in their journey through life.

The director counseled me and helped me do the switch. I started studying social work. This was the best decision I made. This university was well-known for its program, and I fit right in. I studied hard and ended up graduating Magnum Cum Laude with a four-year degree that took me six.

I had vocational rehabilitation (Voc Rehab) and Social Security Disability Insurance (SSDI) to help me financially through my undergraduate degree, but these programs were difficult to maintain while I concentrated on my education. I had to receive special permission from Voc Rehab to be enrolled in eight hours instead of fifteen. I had to take tests proving that not taking a full load of classes was beneficial for me. I had to have a letter from a physician stating my disability.

Once again, I was having to prove what I couldn't do. These tests were to help me prove to Voc Rehab that I was unable to perform at college level right at the time that I was working so hard to prove to myself that I could. Once again, to receive benefits, I was forced to put my deficits into words. Finally, I was given a full-ride scholarship, and I was under the illusion that everyone was at last on my side.

My immediate future now was studying. It's funny how, in 1991, I had positioned my seating in the community college classroom close to one of the sharpest guys in College Algebra. Jeff was my study partner for this class. I might as well have pitched a tent in the math study lab considering all the time I was there. I did end up pitching a tent, so to speak, with Jeff.

Jeff and I eventually graduated from community college together and became first-time parents in tandem. I moved from the historic "Eiker House" into an apartment with Jeff while I carried our child. He and I had some rough times adjusting to our new relationship and with his acceptance of becoming a father.

Jeff would go on long bike rides with a woman friend throughout the metro area and beyond. He told me of his relationship he had formed with his "bicycling partner." I was seven months pregnant when I found out the true nature of the relationship he had developed with this woman. I had been oblivious of why she called the apartment so much. She was very nice to me when she and Jeff were planning their biking trips together that turned into romantic encounters. He moved in with her and left me alone in our apartment to stew over this treatment.

I was so furious that I would call her house looking for Jeff and express my disgust with her, reminding her that he was the father of my unborn child. I couldn't understand how another person could consciously take such steps to "cycle" herself between Jeff and me as we were growing through our rocky relationship. As a result of my hormonal cries of uncontrollable anger, she blocked the phone number of the apartment from which I called. I lived there alone during the final semester for my associate's degree *and* in the final stages of pregnancy.

She was taking steps to prevent my harassing her and anything else that might threaten her developing love affair with the man who had fathered my child. I have forgiven Jeff and he has forgiven me, but I will never forget this trying time.

As my pregnancy neared term, Jeff and I were cordial to each other. We decided on names, attended birthing classes at the hospital where we would be delivering our baby, toured the facility, and went together to his sister's Thanksgiving celebration where I ate three times the amount that I would have had I not been about to give birth. Jeff spent the night in the spare bedroom, and then at 3:00 A.M., we went to the hospital.

I was all-natural in the long birthing process, fifteen hours with no pain medication. I figured that if the pioneers and Indians could do it, surely I could. My mom was worried that the intense pain might cause me to slip back into a coma, being that I was five years post-injury, but she never shared this important information with me until years after that first birth.

Concentration and knowing that this was only a temporary state took me through to the end when my daughter was placed on my chest. Having my mom there to coach me through the process, which she had experienced five times, built my confidence in my ability to do this like a pioneer. She took some graphic pictures of the miracle event, then of Jeff and me holding our new baby. Jeff returned home once the baby was born, but he occupied the other bedroom of our basement apartment. I would not let him, nor did he want to, sleep with Gabrielle and me.

These were rough times. I had had Gabrielle three weeks earlier than my due date. It was a week before finals on Thanksgiving break, during which I had planned to study. Jeff and I didn't know what was normal for a newborn, but this small being, weighing seven pounds, eight ounces at birth, was losing weight before our eyes. She would not latch on to my engorged breasts for feedings.

Three days after her birth, Gabrielle turned yellow and was admitted to Children's Mercy Hospital for jaundice, spending the next three days under bilirubin lights to balance her blood cells and allow her liver to work properly. I spent every spare minute at the hospital, pumping my milk and attempting to feed her while final exams took place. I had to make special arrangements to come back and take my exams to complete my final semester at Penn Valley Community College.

The lactation consultant spent a lot of time with me helping Gabrielle figure out how to eat. My right side and its lack of movement did not build my confidence during this process. Jeff and I ended up renting an electric pump and transferring the correct amount of my milk into a dispenser attached to a long, thin tube draped over my shoulder and taped onto my nipple. Then Gabrielle figured out that there was a reward for her efforts.

Jeff was very supportive in this intensive effort to get Gabrielle nursing correctly. Jeff took turns with my mother and sister watching the newborn Gabrielle, while I had to return immediately to Penn Valley to take my finals. I refused to give Gabrielle a bottle. No doubt my stubborn personality, the trait that had kept me alive five years earlier, bled into my parenting style. I was determined to breast-feed her for the best nutrition and development. This form of feeding ended up being the basis of her diet for next sixteen months.

I refused to let things stand in my way. When our baby girl Gabrielle was nine months old, she and I were on our way to a university about fifty miles away so I could study speech pathology, while Jeff stayed in Kansas City and went to the local university where he had a scholarship. I juggled school, parenting, and an on-again, off-again relationship. I spent my lunches going to the childcare center to nurse, and studied between classes during any free time that I had without Gabrielle. This grew very trying when she became mobile and found she could outrun me at two years-old.

Gabrielle went through all of her first milestones while we were staying in a "family-living" apartment complex on campus. The entire complex must have known her name since all I had to control her behavior was the tone of my voice. During one afternoon while I was preoccupied with organizing my files of notes from every course I was taking that semester, Gabrielle surprised me and completed a couple of important milestones.

When I would get focused on completing a project, it was difficult for me to see though the tunnel vision that my concentration would create. Gabrielle was holding on to furniture while walking, but I never imagined she could do what was about to create a shock wave through the apartment complex. While I organized my notes, Gabrielle completed the milestone of turning her first doorknob and began work on a second milestone that she proudly exhibited for all to see: she went outside and started running down the sidewalk.

After not hearing any noise in the other room for a while, I instinctively went to take a look and see what Gabrielle had gotten herself into. The door was wide open, and I began panicking right away. With a deep roar, I screamed her name but there was no response. I continued to yell for her as I slowly limped to the open area where I could see more of the other apartments along the sidewalk. She was running up the drive of the complex, two or three house-lengths ahead of me as I continued to call her name in a loud and commanding, but now frightened voice.

She looked back at me as I began limping up the sidewalk toward her, gave me a quick smile as if to say "Look what I can do, Mom!" and continued to run away from me. The apartments began spilling out fellow student/parents. It was quite a display of my inability to run and Gabrielle's new ability. As she completed the first block of homes, another mother finally stopped staring and lent a helping hand. She stopped Gabrielle and waited for me to catch up, as I completed this humiliating hobble after my child.

This should have been a day of celebration as my almost two-year-old baby girl, whom I had thought was not yet walking independently, decided to skip a step and go directly from a fast crawl to running. Instead, I was shocked and furious that she had disobeyed my loud commands. At the same time, this event showed me the challenges I had waiting for me, knowing that a two-year old could run faster than I could.

Gabrielle at daycare in Warrensburg, MO
(age 2)

Family
Housing
Celebration
at Central
Missouri
State
University

Gabrielle
visiting
Dad and CC
in Jeff's
Midtown
apartment in
Kansas City,
MO

Coming into the home
stretch at the Amy
Thompson Run for
Daylight.

~CHAPTER FOURTEEN~

Re-determination

It seems to me that our current system of health care benefits works against a person with a disability who is trying to better herself. After five years on Social Security Disability Insurance, I was up for re-determination. This meant that I would be sent to a physician and a psychiatrist of their choice to be reevaluated for eligibility.

I thought the appointments with the psychiatrist went great. I told truthfully of all of my accomplishments: I could carry at least twenty-five pounds, I could walk five miles, and I was successfully going to school. I concentrated on the positive and was proud of all that I had accomplished after being unable to walk or talk just five years earlier.

I forgot to mention that I was capable of carrying twenty-five pounds only because that was how much my daughter weighed at the time, or that I had walked five miles only once, and that was for the Amy Thompson Run to Daylight, a benefit for the Brain Injury Association of Kansas and Greater Kansas City. I had been the last person to cross the finish line—an hour after everyone else—with blisters and joint pain that lasted for two weeks afterwards. Nor did I mention that the only way I could attend college was with the special accommodations I had obtained through Voc Rehab.

No one had warned me that you were supposed to explain to the Social Security Administration (SSA) your condition on your *worst* day. I also learned later on that you can choose your own doctor, and—although they don't tell you this—choosing your own doctor can actually expedite the slow process of getting the reports to SSA. Unaware of the way to work the system and the need to document all of my deficits, I was denied benefits.

Who wants to look at what they can't do instead of working with what they can do? This mindset is beyond me, but a person must remember that the SSA is a huge bureaucracy.

What was I to do? The possibility of my livelihood had been taken away from me before I even got a degree. I had to figure out how to hire a lawyer and re-prove to SSA how desperately I still needed this income and how disabled I continued to be. While I was attending classes and raising a child by myself, I was only able to pay my bills through government programs, and I *depended* on these benefits. Were they now going to be suddenly discontinued? I felt alone with nowhere to turn for assistance and frustrated that my life had taken such an about face.

While I juggled all of these difficult issues, wrote papers, took exams, and slowly made progress in my new major, Gabrielle was constantly getting viruses from daycare. All of this was taking its toll on my ability to concentrate and perform as the student I knew I could be.

Upon advice to obtain legal assistance, I took an uncharacteristic afternoon out of class and found a lawyer. This is when my good friend and lawyer Rob Linscott began helping me. During this potentially huge crisis, he remembered a law that allowed a person to keep her benefits until she had completed her degree program. It was not an easy process, but with Rob's help, and many hour-long drives to get from Warrensburg to our appointments in Kansas City, I was able to get my benefits reinstated until I had earned my degree.

Because I thought I would be cut off from benefits the day I graduated, I scrambled to try and figure out what I would do after graduation. I was frightened that I was going to lose everything, and that my child would suffer. I imagined I was going to fail, as a student and as a mother, and have to live on the Department of Family Services (DFS) for the rest of my adult life.

Finally, I realized that I was listening to negative scenarios and living life with a "glass-is-half-empty" mentality. There were lots of things that were going right. My mom was exercising less and less control over my life, and I was in love with the father of my child. I realized that if all I would let myself see were the negative possibilities, then that would be all that I *could* see. So I once again reminded myself to concentrate on the positives, just as Mom, Carl, and I had done by celebrating with ice cream bars each time I regained more mobility in my paralyzed right extremities.

What I had not realized was that Social Security Disability Insurance (SSDI) is designed to help the disabled population who are having difficulties in returning to work. The system allows a person to work trial periods. When the disabled individual completes six months without losing a job because of his disability, then he is considered not to be disabled any longer and to be working in gainful employment.

I was hired on as a full-time community service worker at the mental health facility where I had completed my internship during my last year at Central Missouri State University. I felt as if I had finally done it: I was living on my own without government assistance!

Being able to move forward in my life was empowering to me. Voc Rehab continued with their assistance and guidance until I got my degree, which I would not have been able to do if I had lost my SSDI.

When all the dust had settled, I received a phone call from a lawyer telling me that the statute of limitations was about to run out on my accident in 1989. I had to be educated on what all of that meant.

It was back and forth to Kansas City once more to learn that I could sue the man who hit me. The lawyer, Gary Leftridge, helped me maneuver through this process, as he worked on contingency. This meant that he would receive 40% of the award from the court's favorable decision, and that he would get nothing if I didn't receive a favorable decision. The person who hit me wanted to settle this case without going to trial. I supposedly could have received more money if I had gone to trial, but that would have meant having to meet the man who had changed my life so suddenly and drastically. I was still very angry at him and felt that I couldn't have kept my composure.

There was also a risk of this man, a lawyer himself, working the legal system in his favor. With all of the decisions that I had to make at this time, I was exhausted and didn't want to drag it out for another possible two years waiting for a court date, so I just settled.

This money allowed me some security, and all I really needed was a car, a vacation, and a down payment on a house. My mother didn't help me with this process. She had begun to let go once I was able to figure out how to regain my own guardianship. Mom wanted nothing to do with suing the person who hit me. She was satisfied and happy that I had survived.

Besides Mom had already been involved in one lawsuit concerning my accident. When I went to live at her house after my release from the hospital, Mom had begun the process of suing Honda for the malfunction of the bolts which held the seat to the car frame. I soon became fixated on the lawyers at this early stage of my recovery. I would call them every day and ask what progress they had made. I quickly grew frustrated with the whole process. I couldn't understand that lawsuits took a lot of time, or that they needed to wait for a court date to be set. I could barely tie my shoes at the time, but I knew how to dial a telephone! I was very self-focused and could think only of my own needs. I was unable to see outside myself.

I only met once with the lawyer who was suing Honda for me. I retained his services and never heard from him again for over six months. I became obsessed because he was not returning my phone messages. I got no reply. I waited and waited, but still no reply. Finally, I fired him.

My actions would have repercussions for my future. My lack of logical thinking had led to the destruction of a court case that, while possibly taking years to resolve, could have set me up for a stress-free future financially.

When I forced myself to look at the positives though, it did seem that, eight years post-injury, my life had taken a dramatic turn for the better. I had earned a bachelor's degree in social work, had a job in mental health, a home, and a happy, healthy, four-year-old daughter. What's more, Jeff decided that he liked being a dad and wanted to build a life together; he finally proposed to me! Yet somehow, I was not happy.

Every day, I traveled through the Missouri countryside to visit a lot of my clientele[2] who lived on farms. I would travel from one client with major depression, to the next with schizophrenia, and on to another with a bipolar disorder. I would then respond to an emergency suicide attempt from a person who was actively hallucinating and get him to agree to be voluntarily hospitalized for observation in order to have his medications reevaluated.

And all of this had to be documented with my left hand.

2 The Mental Health field uses the word "clients," while the term "consumers" is used in the field of Social Work.

Central Missouri State University
College of Education & Human Services
congratulates

Rebekah Dyer

for academic achievement* meriting a place on
The Dean's List
Spring Semester, 1997

*At least 3.5 Grade Point Average
for 12 or more hours.

DEAN

Making the Dean's List at
CMSU (above)

Graduation day with
Gabrielle and Dad
(below)

Graduating with my
Bachelor's Degree (below)

~CHAPTER FIFTEEN~

All Work and No Play

It had become clear that it was time for me to move back to the Kansas City area where I had spent so much of my life. Jeff and I bought a house together in a suburb just a mile from my new employer, communityworks, inc., in Overland Park, Kansas.

I began working with communityworks as a transitional living specialist. I would assist persons who had experienced a TBI, and who either lived, or wanted to live, independently in the community with help from the Home and Community-Based Service (HCBS) Head Injury Waiver in Kansas. I spent a lot of my time driving from one client's home to the next. I would visit up to four hours with each and then go on to the next home. This was quite a fulfilling position, and now at nine years post-injury, I felt I was better able to read frustration signs in my clients and know when to back off and when to push for goal attainment.

I had to be able to remember addresses, phone numbers, and directions to do my job. Oh, and all of the different directions! This just about made me want to give up. I wrote everything down. If I had lost my daily planner, I don't know what would have happened. Those pages contained the overflow that my mind could not hold in short-term memory. It was challenging to keep everything straight. I tried different tactics to help with my problem of being directionally challenged.

I also find that I forget names unless they are part of my routine and I am reminded daily. I use all the tricks and am always open to more. A few of the tricks I use almost daily are: writing things down, setting a timer, keeping up-to-date calendars everywhere, sticky notes, and anything else that can remind me or force me to recall the information that I foresee I will need for future reference.

Technology has been particularly effective in TBI recovery. Therapists are helping persons with brain damage learn how to incorporate small handheld computers, or personal digital assistants (PDAs), into their daily routines. PDAs can be equipped with a digital camera for keeping track of events during the day, carrying on conversations, remembering sequencing and/ or directions, or remembering people's names. Cell phones are also a marvelous and discreet memory tool.

Directions remain difficult for me. Although I *have* gotten better at them with time, I still find it hard to locate my brain's "map page," the page that's supposedly there to help me make sense out of someone's directions. It takes longer for me than most people to do the processing in my head, but the fact is, this struggling provides vital exercise for my brain. By forcing my brain to develop other connections to get me where I'm going, or able to do the task at hand, it aides me in my recovery.

Once I have finally located my "map page," my husband Jeff, usually on the receiving end of my panicked phone calls, frequently adds, "Or you can go..." I refuse to entertain such thoughts, or I will start to get confused all over again. I think he knows this and just likes the reaction I display when I have to push these thoughts out of the way.

When, as a social worker, I was given an address of a home to visit, this would set off a number of my panic buttons. Fellow workers would explain the directions to me, and I would write them down, but it never failed that I would wander in and out of neighborhoods and up and down streets seeking my destination. I used local maps, followed directions, tried to use landmarks as guides, but I just couldn't get any system to work for me.

I was unable to see a picture in my mind while directions were being explained to me. I would make several dry runs with my husband the day before, but I still ended up calling him on his cell phone in a panic and trying to explain my location. I frequently didn't know where I was. I would have to rely on "left" and "right" written instructions.

In *A User's Guide to the Brain*, Ratey writes, "Certain cells in the heads of honey bees and of homing pigeons contain crystals of magnetite, a natural magnetic material. The crystals align in the earth's magnetic field much like the hands of a compass, which is somehow used by these species as a frame of reference in navigating" (Ratey, 109).

Ratey reports that the "same kind of magnetic particles" have been identified in human brain tissue. Even though researchers are not sure if these crystals could have the same function in humans, I still find it a comforting notion that perhaps my lack of direction could be explained by crystals in my brain, dimmed somehow by the trauma of my brain injury.

Whatever I tried, I just couldn't catch my bearings in this new state, even though it was just a street named State Line that separated Kansas from my native Missouri. I couldn't recall any travel experience I had had in this area, due to my impaired long-term memory. My sense of direction certainly hadn't been impaired before my accident. I had moved to Dallas when I was 20-years-old and had no problem finding my way around a strange environment, pretty much effortlessly.

My daily difficulties did have the benefit though of engendering flawless activities that I could use in training my clients and familiarizing them with their community. I knew all of the steps I had to go through, and breaking down these steps and using them to think ahead was a good exercise to get clients to learn the process of getting from point A to point B. I didn't just travel to their homes and stay there the entire time either. I would take them on outings. I used maps to help us understand how to get to an address—for example, the Social Security office, an AA meeting, the local community college, Social and Rehabilitation Services (SRS), or different potential worksites.

These daily adventures were quite a challenge, as I got lost often and didn't know north from south. Once, I was taking a client on a trip to get Christmas supplies from a local food pantry in Kansas City, Kansas in Wyandotte County. There are parts of this city that are definitely not safe, and I happened to be right in the middle of one such part.

I was confused. The person I was assisting had been shot in the head and left for dead two years earlier. I was trying to find a church to help her with food for Christmas dinner, and I felt I had to model self-composure and self-direction for my client. After much internal frustration, I finally pulled over to what looked like a gas station. Instead, it was a liquor store with an attendant who looked at me with irritation the minute I walked in. I proceeded with my question about the location of the church. My client was out in the car unaware of my confusion, while I quickly tried to make sense of the man's directions.

He told me, "Turn east, until you reach a gas station, and turn south, and it should be two blocks up on the southwest corner."

When I asked him politely where east was, he replied, "Well, it's where the sun comes up ever mornin' darlin'."

This was no help at all. I quickly exited this establishment and ended up telling my client of my confusion. It turned out that she knew exactly where we needed to go.

I had had zero confidence in her, especially after her angry outburst while picking up pizza for her family the week before. Her inability to read, to understand communication or to communicate herself had led her to become so frustrated that she screamed gibberish at the attendant in the small carry-out pizza place. But even though she had significant damage to her speech center and had difficulty communicating at the speed of the general public, it turned out that she did not have damage to the area of her brain that gave her memory of directions. This was a lesson for me not to judge a person's abilities based on behavior in certain situations, and to remember that every head injury is different, just as people are.

What Day Is It? — Vandergriff

The Voice
A MEDICAL REHAB NETWORKING NEWSPAPER
Bringing Together Health Care Professionals and Consumers

Poised For The Year 2000 and Beyond

May 1999
Vol. 12, No. 5

Inside this Edition

(small newspaper text, inside-edition listings — illegible)

From left: Karen Fitzpatrick, MA; Janet Williams, Ph.D.; Katie Dallon, MA; Rebekah Vandergriff, BSW. The four spoke at the Florida Brain Injury Association Conference.

Life After Brain Injury
Role Models Offer Advice to Colleagues

(article body text — illegible)

Professionals Give Advice At Brain Injury Conference

(article body text — illegible)

There Is Help

(article body text — illegible)

Articles while working in the rehabilitation field

Advice for managers

SOLUTIONS

Tuesday, March 27, 2001   THE KANSAS CITY STAR   D 21

Agency finds employees among those it serves

Communityworks finds ready source of dedicated staff

BY RUTH BAUMGIES
Special to the Star

The company: Located at 5808 Nall Ave. in Mission, Communityworks Inc. is a rehabilitation agency that helps people with cognitive disabilities to reintegrate into the community. Part of the organization's mission is to help people with brain injuries, particularly injuries resulting from trauma, to maintain independent lives. Vocational rehabilitation, counseling, and speech, occupational and physical therapy are among the services the agency provides. Operating as a fee-for-service organization, Communityworks also provides personal care attendants for clients. Established in 1993, the company has 80 full-time and 68 part-time employees.

■ **Telephone:** (913) 789-9900

■ **Challenge:** Staff retention.

■ **Ownership, top management:** Owner and president Janet Williams leads a 15-member management team.

■ **Background:** Working with people who have experienced brain injury has its challenges, Williams said. Employees must be available to work weekends and evenings, she said, and need to have a certain level of understanding and compassion to help their clients regain a degree of independence.

Finding employees willing to make such a commitment hasn't been easy, Williams said. The level of wages Communityworks could offer has been another stumbling block to employee retention.

"Front-line workers were making $8 an hour, and that's not much," she said.

Communityworks also lost employees who came on board in May after school was out, but then left in September to return to their studies.

"It was a revolving door," Williams said. "We were putting a lot of money into training and then losing them."

Williams and her management team decided they had to be creative in order to compete for employees in a tight labor market.

"We had to find something that was beyond the money," she said. "We had to look for the passion."

■ **Action:** In the past, former Communityworks clients had indicated they wanted to work with others with brain injuries. After several staff meetings to discuss the employee retention issue, Williams said the idea of hiring such workers

(continued — right column)

surfaced as a viable solution. "They've been there and had the passion," Williams said. "We thought, 'Here we are trying to get these people jobs. How could we go to an employer and ask them to hire these folks if we don't?' It's role modeling," Williams said.

Using word-of-mouth and newspaper advertising, Communityworks sought potential employees who had had brain injuries. Applicants were put through a standard screening process to make sure they could handle the work responsibilities. Those selected went through the regular training program to learn how to work with brain-injured clients. They also were trained in policies and procedures to follow on the job.

Those hired were matched with clients and taught the individual protocols to follow. Williams realized some employees might need extra help themselves because of their own injuries. "We get to know what their needs are and make accommodations as needed," she said.

Since 1997, when Communityworks started this effort, seven individuals with brain injuries have joined the staff. Of these, three were former clients of the organization. Of the 15-member management team, Williams said three have had brain injuries.

■ **Results:** Williams said employee retention has increased since hiring individuals with brain injuries. "We've held on to people longer, and we've kept all the people we've hired with brain injuries," Williams said.

There have been other dividends as well.

"We're seeing a huge increase in staff sensitivity," she said. "It's providing perspective to the staff."

124

~CHAPTER SIXTEEN~

The Medical Model vs. Independent Living

As I did my research in preparation for this book: going through my papers, sending out questionnaires, talking to family and friends; I came across several letters that were created as my future was being decided for me. These letters are excellent examples of the terminology used by the medical model. The first is to a lawyer, in support of my mother's request to obtain Power of Attorney. It uses all of the medical jargon that is usually necessary for documentation purposes. Dated on the day of my accident, and signed by my mother and my family physician, it reads:

I _The Family Physician, MD_ being of lawful age and duly sworn upon my oath, state that on June 3, 1989, Rebekah Dyer was involved in an automobile accident at _____ where in she sustained serious injuries leaving her in a coma, said coma causing her to be incapacitated. That I am the treating physician of said Rebekah Dyer and feel that she needs a power of attorney to act in behalf so long as she's in an incapacitated state. This general power of attorney shall include all necessary acts, to manage her daily affairs and specifically authorize the attorney-in-fact to release the 1987 Honda CRX from the Kansas City Missouri tow lot at 1st and Lydia and to do any other acts necessary dealing with the release of this automobile. As Rebekah's Dyer's treating physician I hereby appoint Sharon Eiker as the Attorney-in-fact to do any and all of the above mentioned acts.

As I dug deeper, I unfolded another a letter written according to the medical model. This one was dated *after* I had already passed the "magical" six- to twelve-month period of rehabilitation, the period after which you're not expected to make any more improvements. Since many doctors believe that this is when most TBI survivors plateau, having achieved all they will be able through rehabilitation, it can become a self-fulfilling prophesy. But it doesn't have to be. This period is *their* unit of measurement; while *we*, the ones who have survived the un-imaginable, know better.

This letter was signed by my doctor of Physical Medicine and Rehabilitation on April 7th of 1993. It was requested for my defense in the petition to relieve my mother of her duty to be my Guardian and reads:

This is to acknowledge that I have been involved in the care of Rebekah Dyer since her involvement in a vehicular accident, being originally admitted to our hospital on 6/3/89.

The patient, who is a white female, has been under my care since. Our last formal evaluation was in January of 1991 and I did authorize driving testing and training on 10/1/92. The patient incurred a closed head injury with subdural hematoma on the left and multiple potate intraparaenchyma hemorrhages which altered her thinking for a period of time. As of our last visit, however, she was well oriented, was in school and appeared to be able manage her affairs. The patient was successful in completing her driving training in October of 1992. In my opinion, she has regained her capacity to manage her affairs and would no longer need guardianship or formal assistance in managing her personal or financial affairs.

When my mother was going through the process of obtaining guardianship rights, she had been informed of the social services providing assistance in the state of Missouri for persons with disabilities. The hospital provided a social worker who assisted with applying for Social Security Disability Income for me, paying the hospital bills, arranging for the outpatient therapies, and with contacting a lawyer. This was a difficult time for my family, and the social worker had to be sensitive to our issues. She made certain that I was being discharged into a safe environment and recommended a psychologist for me to be involved with after my hospital stay.

Regarding this guardianship, Mom later explained to me, "When you can figure out how to regain your own guardianship, I will know that you have improved enough to manage your own business."

In 1989, as a resident of Missouri, I could not take advantage of the waiver system that was available to Kansas residents. I now recognize, as a person who has experienced a severe TBI and then been educated as a social worker in the field, the difference that the waiver has made in the lives of persons who qualify for the service.

A lot has happened to get me to where I am today. My purpose in documenting all of this is to demonstrate the difference between the medical model of thinking and the independent living model.

The medical model of treatment can create a dependency on the system, as the person who has experienced a TBI begins to rely on the system to "fix" all his problems: therapists to discover a remedy, or doctors to find a cure. It may be at this point when we who have experienced brain injuries should question the medical model. Professionals who treat patients with TBIs often stereotype us. They think that we are noncompliant, exhibit inappropriate behavior, and lack judgment; and that this is a result of the brain injury, not a result of inappropriate institutionalization. Even some who finally get to the point where they think they have proven themselves, that they are able to be trusted enough to be independent and considered as adults again, are *not* given their rights as adults. Then they must deal not only with their disabling condition, but also with the need to maneuver through these systems—which requires a certain amount of ability and resourcefulness. The institution providing care may often doubt the patient's ability to care for himself simply because they do not want to become liable to future legal action if this turns out to be the wrong decision.

At this juncture in recovery, the patient and his family need to start thinking like *consumers*—a word we often use to refer to them. They have become aware of the permanence of the disability, and now they need to become aware of their rights. This can be unrealistic, of course, depending on the cognitive skills of the patient and personal resources of the family.

A person can even find himself vacillating between the medical model and the independent living model because of where funding is available. It is therefore important that the patient and his family begin to understand that there is a difference between the two models: with the medical model, the outcome is a complete cure or compliance with continued treatment; while, with the independent living model, the outcome is quality of life.

The independent living philosophy is a shift away from the authoritarian style of the medical model to a paradigm of individual empowerment. This is when *we* show our own responsibility, *we* show that we have the ability to redefine ourselves, and to provide the basic components to meet our *own* needs.

During my 2½ month hospital stay, I was a cognizant patient in two interdisciplinary meetings, and yet was not included in the decisions being made about my future after my release. The team of professionals focused on preparing my family for my limited ability to live on my own. In retrospect, the only options my family had were an inpatient rehabilitation facility in Mount Vernon, Missouri, or for me to go live with one of my parents. My mother reports that one of the team members had advised her against institutionalizing a person recovering from a coma state. This allowed her to make the necessary arrangements for me to do my rehabilitation as an outpatient.

My mother had this to say about how she made it through those difficult days:

Only once did I lose it in the hospital. Only once did I feel so helpless that I sat down and cried. The nurses brought a gurney that had moveable parts. They rolled her onto it to take her to physical therapy. It bent in the middle and at the knees, then two side wings held her head. She rolled her head against the brace on one side and began to drool with her mouth open and her eyes unfocused. And I thought, "Oh my God we have such a long way to go."

You never know if you have the strength to finish a trial. When you see something stretch out way into the future you must pace yourself or you won't finish. That afternoon I geared down and dug in for the long haul. My vision cleared by tears.

The dilemma experienced by a TBI survivor, once she has adopted the independent living philosophy, and is living independently, is convincing the people in her environment of her ability, and learning to direct the support system that provides her assistance. This helping staff may be family, part of an Independent Living Center (ILC), or the staff of a Home and Community Based Service.

Research is necessary to discover what services are available before the person ventures from the institution out into the community. Funding only pays for health-related challenges and this causes the medical model to become predominant in a person's life. An individual is forced to continue her sick role in order to receive money for services—if she regains too much ability, she can lose very services that help her expand her abilities and maintain what she has. This is a catch-22.

When a person receives health care he expects the practitioner to essentially make him "feel better." At times, this requires addressing problems that are not only physiological but also social, psychological, or at times all systems combined. Eventually, it is both essential and practical that the team of practitioners allow the patient to address his own areas of concern regarding his recovery.

The moment a person slips into a coma her entire life is drastically altered. The survivor will encounter many professionals in many disciplines geared to assist with rehabilitation goals. The patient and her family will be exposed to these professionals throughout the hospital stay; and afterwards, as they meet periodically to discuss treatment issues and future plans. The goal is for the head-injured person to return to as full of a life as possible. The variety of health care specialists that the patient and family can encounter include: Neurosurgeon, Neurologist, Consulting Physicians, Physiatrist, Neuropsychologist, Occupational Therapist, Speech and Language Pathologist/Cognitive Therapist, Rehabilitation Psychologist, Rehabilitation Nurse, Social Worker, Physical Therapist, Recreation Therapist, Psychiatrist, Nutritionist/Dietician, and Vocational Rehabilitation Counselor.

Once the therapies of the acute phase have reached their goals, the patient progresses to the post-acute phase. The post-acute phase of rehabilitation may be provided in a hospital setting, rehabilitation hospital, rehabilitation center or facility specializing in head injury rehabilitation, a nursing home, or in the patient's own home.

The process of this rehabilitative stage may take months or up to several years. It seems as though the length of this period of rehabilitation depends on funding as much as, or even more than, the extent of the brain injury.

The dilemma is to understand when this point of transition is ready to take place. The traditional process is that the patient taken from the rehabilitation unit, then transferred to another wing of the same hospital, a residential care facility, or a nursing home. This was before the advent of the independent living philosophy. Now the survivor, family, and staff have options.

Who advocates for the person who has survived a brain injury? This is where the social work staff can help, through their acquaintance with programs and monies set aside for just this purpose. The real work is convincing staff or family by educating them in the knowledge and belief that their loved one can survive without the assistance of the hospital/medical environment.

Timing of the independent living phase is different in each person's situation. Based on their attitude and stamina, it may be possible to provide all medical attention in home. The decision to be made is when the time is appropriate for the person in question to live without being in a protected environment and dependent on the medical system.

There are programs available to help arrange for a survivor of a Traumatic Brain Injury to live in his own home with visiting nurses, including physical, speech, and occupational therapists coming there for sessions. Other professionals can provide training in independent living skills in a variety of settings when he is ready to go out into the community. Significantly, all of this support can be provided in-home at *a fraction of the cost* it would be at a facility, and *at the same level of treatment.*

Taking on the role of the consumer can be empowering for the injured and his family at this stage of rehabilitation. They can choose which staff to employ to assist them, instead of, as is usually the case with a patient in a hospital, simply being treated by whichever doctor happens to be on the ward that day.

With many professionals working toward the same goal there are potential areas of confusion in defining roles. There are many factors that the survivor, family or guardian must consider when dealing with such an involved set of circumstances. With the array of services offered in rehabilitation, the patient has potential of becoming lost in the decision-making processes.

At what point should community reintegration be introduced? Community re-entry is perhaps the most challenging phase of recovery from head injury. The efforts made while in the medical system may lose their impact if the individual is discharged into a setting that cannot meet long-term care needs. There have been strong strides toward improving lives of people with disabilities. It is now time that the environment be made congruent with the needs of the individual, and assistance provided to the survivor who requests rehabilitation in her own community.

With the advent of the ADA (American with Disabilities Act), a change has taken place in societal attitudes. Accessibility to businesses and educational institutions has improved greatly, and the changes have created a more accepting environment for persons with disabilities who wish to live independently.

After surviving a coma or brain injury, coming home to a familiar environment with family is the ideal situation. However, many families have fears about bringing them back into the home; in part, because they equate hospitals with being able to fix their loved one. A family's main concern is often that they will be unable to keep up with the level of care that a hospital can provide. They may feel inadequate when faced with the task.

I understand why a family can feel this way. Many families cannot provide the 24-hour care that is sometimes necessary at a certain point in recovery.

A family does make a huge sacrifice by bringing their loved one back home, but many states now have home health care that can do just as well as a hospital. Plus, if there is a Head Injury Waiver system set up in their state, a Medicaid-eligible individual can do many therapies in the home, including: physical, occupational, speech, and cognitive therapy; and even psychological counseling as needed. Sometimes family members are even trained to change feeding tubes or IV fluids.

By 1990, there were over 150 waiver programs nationwide, targeting elders, people with physical and developmental disabilities, and people with the human immunodeficiency virus (HIV) infection. HCBS has made community re-entry a reality for many survivors who are in institutions or at risk of institutionalization.

All the services of the Head Injury Waivers are provided in the person's own home. When I was researching this area, there were only five states: Kansas, Minnesota, Washington, New Jersey, and California, that had Medicaid waivers for people with TBI in operation, and at least two additional states—New York and New Hampshire, that had waivers in the works.

The services that the Head Injury Waiver is able to provide to consumers have revolutionized rehabilitation from TBI. Just my luck, that it was Kansas that obtained the first Home and Community-Based Services Medicaid Waiver specifically for persons with head injuries. At my time of injury, Kansas residents between the ages of 18 and 55 who had experienced an open or closed head injury, were Medicaid eligible, and at risk of living in an institution were eligible. Kansas *got* it.

Kansas gave us back our independence! They realized and then put into place the basis for the Kansas waiver program that provides independent living skills training, also known as transitional services. The independent living specialist is able to work with a person up to 4 hours a day, 7 days a week. A range of other waiver services is available including therapies, case management (resource facilitation), medical attendants, non-medical (personal care) assistants, night support, durable medical equipment, and medic alert as well as regular Medicaid services. Kansas, the very state next to my then-home state of Missouri, was providing a service that I wish I could have been able to take advantage of as a consumer.

It seemed as though this was an ideal program of services for the person who qualifies for Medicaid, but I had insurance. Would that have affected my ability to take advantage of these services?

I found this program too late—after I had obtained my first degree. Because I had insurance, it wouldn't have mattered, the insurance company is billed for services that the person receives, then the insurance company must write a letter of denial before Medicaid will pay the provider. This third party liability takes time and is an arduous task of home health care providers.

A licensed home health care agency may provide many services to persons who have experienced a TBI. An agency can provide case management, transitional living specialists, as well as therapists trained in cognitive, occupational, physical, and speech therapies. By 1998, I was fully employed, and the agency I was working with provided all of the medical attention, plus offered peer and family support groups, drug and alcohol counseling, and continues to offer personal assistants, and connections to other community resources.

Janet Williams, PhD developed an organization that is dedicated to assisting people to live, work and play in their community since the beginning of the Kansas Home and Community Based Waiver System in 1990. Communityworks, inc. began working with over a hundred individuals and families helping them reach their goals, and now that number is in the thousands.

I participated on many interdisciplinary teams as a Transitional Living Specialist at communityworks. The problems I discovered in being on such a team was that they tend to be formed on the basis of convenience, i.e. whoever is available and willing to participate determines who is included on the team. There are many variables that can make a difference in the team's input and output, such as the team's frequency in meeting, intensity, and type, as well as their contact with the consumer and his family.

The point at which the treatment team became involved in the person's life is also of paramount importance. This may take place at any time or phase from intake through discharge at a facility, in the home, or in only one of these phases. When a person begins the HCBS Waiver can be a deciding factor in what they can get out of the program. The deciding factor of when the Head Injury Waiver will cease is when there is no progress being made toward the person becoming more independent.

This is an exciting time for TBI rehabilitation and a time for potential change for Missouri, such as Dr. Janet Williams has advocated in front of the Missouri legislature at the Department of Health. She hopes to encourage constituents to contact their legislature and promote activity that will bring a Medicaid Head Injury Waiver program to their state.

I became very familiar with the Medical Model vs. Independent Living Model, and with Cognitive Therapy, Social Work, Interdisciplinary Teams, and the HI waiver. This exploration gave me insight into the mystery of head injury.

There continues to be a lack of public education about rehabilitation from TBI. This field remains in a malleable stage of its development. It is time for change in the concept of what a person can be able to do after a TBI, and dedicated rehabilitation professionals and family can make a difference.

The totality of losses is something that I don't want to concentrate on. I realize that my wiring has changed as well as my priorities in life. I realize that it is too much work to lie, and besides, I'm not good at it any more. In addition, when I compare the process of going through life playing mind games and lying to get what you want to that of going through life saying what you mean and getting or not getting what you really want honestly, I have to conclude that life is too short not to enjoy the fruits of an honest and caring nature.

Even my emotional responses are different from what they were before my trauma. Damage to my limbic system, the emotional center of the brain, has rewired them. I often find myself laughing when I should cry. When I was pregnant and my hormones were going awry, my daily laugh attacks became tiring.

At times, crying would really help another person be able to understand how I feel and hear my pain. My laughing instead doesn't help anything, and it has happened at times that were really inappropriate, like at a funeral. My strategy now is just to hide my face and try not to make any sounds. The side-effects of TBI are different in everyone and often keep improving with time.

I have a dimple on my right cheek that is a sure giveaway of my emotions. This dimple disappeared for at least six months from my hemiparesis of facial nerves. I forgot that I even had a dimple on my cheek, then one day it was there. I saw my smile spread slightly to the right side of my face and knew this milestone would be cause for another ice cream bar celebration!

In addition to my smile muscles, I also have to pay close attention to my occasional drooling. I know I slur my speech when I'm tired. Half of my face still remains numb, as if I had had dental work and endured a shot of Novocaine. My teeth were cracked and splintered in the accident. I have had two root canals, including a complete loss of one tooth—but luckily only one.

I have difficulty finding words to express myself in conversations. This uncomfortable lack of speed in speech causes some people to fill in words for me. I willingly accept any efforts to relieve their need for speed.

There are several areas of our brains that could affect the word-finding process if damaged and scientists have defined each with a different name. Using graphs that I found in several different texts on this subject, I figured out that I suffered from Wernicke's aphasia, named for the man who discovered that this part of the brain affects *mostly* words for objects. With the brain's plasticity, it can break through scar tissue or whatever else is causing the delay in speech. It has been detected through Magnetic Resonance Imaging (MRI) that there are six different areas of the brain that help us think of a word. The brain can even switch to the other hemisphere to assist us in our quest for information. This takes time and determination for a person to get their brain to make these connections.

Our society wants everything fast. People want information as fast as their computers can process it. They want their pizza delivered within twenty minutes, a wait at their doctor's office that doesn't exceed fifteen, and their money retrieved instantaneously from the nearest ATM. I have had to accept that I no longer work at the warp speed that society would rather deal with.

Before the invention of debit cards, I had to fill out checks at establishments where there were many of the "warp speed" type clientele behind me in line. I would forget the date—even the year sometimes—how to spell the words for the amount and, not to mention, the man whom I married has eleven letters in his last name! This would make it take even longer for me to write, and patience was just not an attribute shared by the people behind me in line.

My slow walking or writing would cause heavy sighs of irritation and impatience. One lady got so close to me once that I could feel her deep gasps of air going in and out, as she made sure that her hot breath hit my neck, so I could physically, as well as emotionally, feel *her* frustration—along with my own— as I was forced to ask the cashier, "What day is it?"

Some people would choose the tactic of shuffling their feet to express their impatience. As a result of all this, I became accustomed to writing out as much as I could of my check before I went into a store where I knew that I would be buying anything. I always hope that I won't forget how to spell the cost. I use any tactic I can to help relieve this uncomfortable tension behind me in line. I am always surprised at the smiles of sympathy a cane creates as I am limping my way through the aisles or waiting in line to pay.

I was right-handed before the TBI, and now I have to do everything with my left. I have double vision, broken collarbones, and the loss of response from the right side of my body due to my hemiplegia. I get little help from my right side to do large motor movement activities, but I know how much worse it could be, and how much better it has gotten over the years. I try not to dwell on the losses. I have dealt with the results of my unusual gait for almost twenty years, and it has taken its toll on my body. The list could go on and on, but these are all just the visible damages. There is not one of my physical challenges that means more to me than the damage that was inflicted on my cognition.

All of these physical problems will constantly be seen by the medical community as apparent challenges they must attempt to conquer. I choose to not perceive myself as broken. The cost of my having to remain in rehabilitative therapy for the rest of my life is insurmountable. A physical rehabilitation doctor diagnosed me as displaying hemi-neglect and wrote a prescription for physical therapy, 16 years post-injury. I will go, the way I always have since the accident, listen to the suggestions, and take home the exercise sheets. I do include my right side, but it has shrunk in muscle tone, and the atrophy is apparent to see.

I realize that everyone reaches a point of saying, "Okay, I am disabled. Now, let's figure out what I can do to make my life meaningful and worth getting out of bed for." I am frustrated at the lack of response throughout the years from my right hand. I know I am fortunate that I have gotten as far as this. *If I now do everything with my left hand, so what?* At one point, the diagnosis was that my right hand would never have any movement for the rest of my life as it remained clenched in a fist held tightly to my right side.

All of the doctors and therapists I've encountered want to fix me. It feels as if they don't listen to my concerns about cost and the need to give my children constant care, and they refuse to let me cope with the remaining difficulties of the trauma I survived. The medical community will forever want to work with the right side of my body, so it is my responsibility to communicate to a doctor that I accept my disability and "enough is enough."

F.O.O.D. for THOUGHT
INGREDIENTS FOR LIFE POST TBI
BY
REBEKAH VANDERGRIFF LMSW

FAMILY:
1. PARTICIPATION
2. INTEREST
3. CONCERN

OPTIMISM:
1. MAINTAINING A POSITIVE ATTITUDE
2. BELIEVE IN ABILITIES / FUTURE
3. CREATE REALISTIC AND OBTAINABLE GOALS

OPTIONS:
1. SCHOOL
2. JOB
3. COMMUNITY SERVICES

DETERMINISM:
1. ABILITY TO STAY ON TASK
2. KEEP UP THE INTEREST
3. STUBBORN ATTITUDE

Example of a TBI workshop.

Left:
Struggling to zip up
Camille.

Below:
Camille visits Olivia
in the hospital
on the day of her
birth

Olivia Josette

May 24, 2003

8lbs. 14oz.

141

The Vandergriffs at
Christmas, 2003.
L to R: Jeff, Olivia,
Gabrielle, Camille,
Rebekah

Above:
Debbie holds Gabrielle
(8 mos.) at the Kansas City Jazz
and Blues Festival.

~CHAPTER SEVENTEEN~

The Journey Continues

August 2, 1989
A Mother's View:

When we were preparing to leave the hospital to reenter the world, we were excited. Dr. Kelly had given Rebekah a list of therapies to keep up with as an outpatient. They included speech, occupational, and physical therapy. There was even water therapy, and I had secured a psychiatrist to assist Rebekah in her social life.

We didn't choose to go to a sheltered home for further recovery, even though we had checked out several such places and our insurance would have covered the treatment. They seemed so sterile and hopeless. We were going out into the real world and take our chances. Dr. Kelly had told Rebekah life would be her daily treatment as she met each new challenge. Dr. Kelly then took me aside and suggested I get Rebekah's tubes tied before we left the hospital. When I asked why, he said, "Head-injured girls can't seem to think of a reason to say 'no' to sex." I answered, "I don't want to make that decision for Rebekah. I will keep a close eye on her." Little did I know what a big job that would be.

Rebekah did have an unexpected pregnancy while she was in junior college. Abortion was suggested, but I could only celebrate new life when, not too long ago, death was looming.

It was difficult for Rebekah to go to school and be a single mother. However, like the true champion she is, Rebekah beat the odds and not only graduated with an AA degree but graduated with honors.

Having a baby gave Rebekah a boost towards independence. She got her own place and became a mother who was depended on by a small child, rather than a daughter who depended on her mother. That was no small feat.

As Rebekah moved towards having her own place, I insisted she would have to sue me for her guardianship. This required a judge, a social worker, and several doctors to defend her case for guardianship. She also had to secure a lawyer. I figured if she could pull all that off, she was able to launch a new life on her own. She was fearless, organized and insistent. She prevailed.

I never accepted the easy way out. People were fond of telling me short and sweet statements like, "Honey, there is a plan for you. That is why you have this disability." But I knew I had a huge task to accomplish: I had to relearn everything and recreate my entire existence using a mind and body that had been radically altered. My life had been transformed into a long series of embarrassing moments and confusion.

Every morning during my years at the Eiker House, I would wake up wondering what day it was. I would lie in bed trying to remember what I had done the day before. Testing myself, I tried to force myself to recall without using the tools I had been taught in therapy. Until finally, I would get frustrated and have to get up and go look at my calendar—which I updated nightly with a slash—or go read my journal entry from the day before. Today, I understand that what I was doing each morning, without my even realizing it or knowing the proper medical terminology for it, was a good exercise for my brain. Through the struggle new connections were being made.

Proudly displaying my Master's hood at
Kansas University.

But besides the daily mundane struggles that a person with a disability has to face, there are the highly personal ones that almost no one wants to talk about. Sex is one of these. I can only say how thankful I am that my mom did not listen to the doctor and have me sterilized. My three wonderful daughters would not be here today!

Many parents hope that their child with a brain injury will simply not have any sexual feelings, or perhaps they just can't imagine them having any. As a social worker, I often encountered an attitude among colleagues, and even in the literature of the profession, that labeled any sexual expression as a "behavior problem" that needed to be extinguished. The articles usually then go on to suggest ways to accomplish this.

As a coping mechanism, some people who are accustomed to having to attend therapy sessions have learned ways to say what the therapist wants to hear. The result of such a session is that everyone goes home happy. The therapist is happy because their client finally said what they were supposed to, indicating the sessions have been a success; and the client is happy because he gets to graduate from this round of meetings. Everybody seems to get what they want, but the person who needed the therapy is left with their pain.

I've witnessed the internalized pain of survivors due to the lack of attention and care paid to their sexuality. This internalized pain can cause depression and, if not treated, the hopeless feeling that suicide is the only alternative. The cycle can go round and round as unaddressed sexual issues cause depression that leads to repeated suicide attempts.

For a person who experiences any disability or developmental delay, their painfully honest, up-front approach; coupled with a lack of socially appropriate ways to communicate their feelings, can be red warning lights that cause caregivers to shut down emotionally out of fear or to try to practice avoidance.

The "stop thought process" technique is employed by many in this field. An example of this technique is when the caregiver changes the topic quickly. But this can only work for so long before the issue must be addressed, so that more communication barriers are not formed. It can even send a message to someone that they are "bad" for having what are perfectly normal sexual thoughts or reactions. It can also lead to further confusion, perhaps leaving him wondering why he is ignored when he talks about his feelings "down there"?

The caregiver is probably unaware of these unintentional messages or the damage they cause. All the client knows is that he feels messages of discomfort from his caregivers or therapists. Imagine a person who needs 24-hour assistance trying to communicate these uncomfortable urges. Then imagine if it were you trying to make sense of all the feedback you were receiving from helping professionals, as you tried to make sense of why your sex organ is pulsating. What can a person, who has difficulty communicating any way, do when confronted with an issue that many people find difficult to talk about in the best of settings—when all the while, their brain keeps innocently causing this crisis of emotions by continuing to release sex hormones into their system?

I'm hoping that I can help bring sexual issues, and their connection to depression and suicide, out into the open, and that this openness can create a forum to assist families, professionals, and medical staff in understanding why persons who survive physical trauma to the brain might appear insensitive, inappropriate, or even perverted at times.

It is common that social rule-breaking happens after a head injury. It is also assumed that the person may no longer have the ability to judge how others are interpreting their actions. The extent of the injury to the brain determines the survivor's ability to be diligent and motivated to regain socialization in appropriate ways to communicate.

Extremely troubling to me is that counselors sometimes refuse to work with certain clients for fear of being inappropriately spoken to or touched. Perhaps if we helped therapists address their own feelings about sexuality, they would be better equipped to deal with clients who express their sexuality during sessions. This may help therapists recognize the potential for misrepresentation and take steps to remedy the situation.

I don't mean to imply, however, that a person who has experienced a disabling accident should be excused from responsibility for his or her behavior. I say: teach a person struggling with issues of a sexual nature what is, and is not, acceptable behavior right from the beginning—it is important to be consistent. They should gently but firmly be told how their actions are being interpreted.

While there is a time early in recovery from a brain injury when behaviors are unconscious, I believe that as a person is becoming aware of the ramifications of their actions, they should be held responsible for how they are communicating these feelings. Communication is a huge frustration for many people recovering from TBI, blast injuries, or even mild brain trauma; and it can be equally frustrating for the people with whom this survivor interacts on a daily basis.

Perhaps role modeling could be used to demonstrate how they could act or react in a situation, and also how not to act. Every person reacts differently when the issue of sex is brought up. Some might feel comfortable talking about it, some may not have impulse control and continue to grab at the therapist's breast, while simply having thoughts of a sexual nature might embarrass another person. There are also people at the other end of the spectrum, who may be at the stage where all they know is hitting, screaming, or giggling to get their point across.

I have heard stories of TBI survivors masturbating in public, exposing themselves to children, or placing their hands on female nursing staff in inappropriate ways. Many professionals feel that simply ignoring this behavior will cause it to go away. However ignoring it just prolongs the individual's ignorance of it, and a "teachable moment" can be lost. They need to be taught that there are consequences for their behavior. My lesson, for example, was when my mother took me out of the hospital coffee shop after I had removed my shirt in public. I was growing especially tired of hospital food, and when I was forced to eat back in my room instead of getting the deli sandwich I had been craving, it made an impression.

The rehabilitation process is as different for each individual as was the cause of injury. However, rehabilitation of physical or mental disabilities typically does not even address—let alone have a goal plan—for issues of sexuality; which is odd, given the amount of importance survivors place on it. It is simply easier for the medical profession, care givers, family and society all to address adults with physical or intellectual disabilities as if they were nonsexual.

This totally overlooks the reality that the question, "Will I ever have sex again?" is usually of paramount concern in the minds of the newly injured. I once witnessed a doctor ask a panel of people with paraplegia (paralysis of the lower body) if they had to decide between being able to walk again or having normal sexual function, which they would choose. Most people chose sex over walking, exemplifying the importance of sexual contact to our human nature, and having "all the parts work right."

Sexuality is an excellent example of an integrative function. Satisfying this basic human need requires a person to integrate their physical signs with the ability to adequately express their feelings, to integrate sexual communication and intimacy. Having the ability to trust another person is an additional ingredient in this complex recipe. You must also be able to express the ingredients of sensitivity, creativity, patience, and, when appropriate, to mix in a sense of humor. Sex is a difficult recipe to prepare and many people have trouble with it.

Just putting the correct sequence of thoughts into words can be a challenge for TBI survivors. Is it any wonder loved ones end up believing that sexual expression is just not on the menu of possibilities for the survivor?

Expressing one's sexuality is a complex function for our brains to perform. It accesses many different areas at once in our brains. My mother has always talked openly with me about sex; so when I told her about a dream I had which resulted in an orgasm, she was thrilled. She then began talking with me about decisions I could make in this area. Once again, she used my experience as a teaching tool. After such trauma to my brain, she had been doubtful that I would ever have such feelings again. Indeed, it was about two years after my brain trauma until I had sexual feelings with a partner. My mother was even happier when I told her that I was having sex again. I know that sounds strange, but she is aware of all the intricate connections the brain performs while doing its acrobatic moves to connect neurons, release chemicals, and signal dendrites through the lightning connections that must happen to have an orgasm.

Unfortunately, most people are not as comfortable with discussing sexuality as my mother is. It seems our society cannot even say "sex" without lowering its tone and whispering the word. Still I don't understand how we can assume that an injured person will be able to internally accept their situation and form a new sexual identity without any help. Inability to function sexually can become a stumbling block to regaining one's self-esteem. Yet our society expects an individual to do all of the essential recovery work alone and in secret.

It's a volcano of emotions waiting to erupt. I am of the opinion that sexuality should be routinely addressed as a part of the rehabilitation process, that is, if the injured can hear the suggestions and is not religiously restrained from discussing it. Sexual expression is something that needs to be worked on like everything else. If the individual cannot share the experience with another person, an alternative expression should be discussed, and masturbation or a different form of sexual expression can be suggested.

During the time when I worked to help TBI survivors relearn their living skills, I worked with an 18-year-old girl. She and I had built a solid foundation in our relationship so that we could feel comfortable having personal discussions. She told me of her past sexual experiences and her desire to have sex again. I suggested that she choose another way of having an orgasm. We discussed that touching yourself in a private setting is completely normal. She wasn't disgusted with this idea, so I further explained that there is nothing wrong with this form of expression, and then we discussed how she could get some privacy in her small house, and appropriate times that she could take advantage of. This seemed doable but not exactly easy because there were others sharing her bedroom. Since incurring her disability, she now had 24-hour care, in case she experienced a problem during the night. This lack of privacy is a prime example of the sort of depersonalization that characteristically happens following a disability.

There are many people who continue to think that masturbation should not be talked about. If her mom knew we were talking about this form of self-expression, I could see her having me fired. Yet with someone's well-being possibly at stake, this conversation can be too crucial not to have.

The point I am trying to drive home is that just because you have had an accident, experienced some brain damage, or TBI does not mean that you are now asexual.

However, to become sexually healthy, someone must overcome both their own and others' expectations that sexual performance will be just as before. Expectations have to be brought back in line with current sexual capacities.

It's a difficult territory to navigate. In fact, I had a relationship break up that really could have had a future. For about a year after my accident, I dated a man who knew me from when I was 17. I guess it was me who had broken up with him all those years ago, and he couldn't figure out how or why I could have changed my mind and wanted to get back together now. Of course, he knew I had brain trauma. He even expressed to me that he felt like he was taking advantage of me because I was now in a disabled body. Nevertheless, I couldn't help him understand what I felt because I had difficulty finding the words. I also was slurring a great deal at this juncture in my healing process. Even so, I realized that I could never be the person I was before, nor did I want to compete with her. I had to redefine myself, and my experience, while trying not to get depressed along the way. I ended up burying myself in rehabilitation and school.

I realize from my research the complexities involved in the sexual response cycle and the different areas of the brain that control all of its intricate functioning. Exposure to information on sexuality issues has and will continue to benefit anyone who has a disabling injury. Of course, part of that is dependent on the ability to find someone willing to talk—be it a family member, social worker, medical staff, or counselor. Someone who will listen with empathic ears and help you address this hidden, yet biologically essential topic.

Besides sexuality, there are other areas of identity loss that can cause an injured person to become depressed. It is not unusual for someone to feel they've lost who they are. They may have lost material items that they've spent their whole lives collecting, maybe even a loved one, or perhaps their own personality, once so glowing. They may never have considered the possibility that life could be so ruthless, when suddenly all aspects of their former life are gone. Moreover, if all of your spare time is spent in daily therapy exercises hoping for some improvement or reaction from an unresponsive section of your body, it isn't hard to see how one could become depressed. I have experienced this depression, and it is not pretty. Those emotions try their hardest to convince every fiber of your being to go down the path of no-return and self-destruction.

I will never forget the days when it took everything I had left to pry my body out of bed. My head would barely poke through thick, dark, oily clouds that hovered around my bed each morning as my mother helped me get up and around. Every day she had to shine a light on something for me to look forward to—an event, an appointment, even a phrase—anything that could get me moving and out of my bed. I just wanted to give up and lie there, waiting to sink into the earth, but my mother let me know that every day, everything, everywhere, were tasks for me to do and experiences to comprehend.

All types of depression can and should be addressed through therapy. Typical options can include drug or cognitive therapy, or perhaps a combination of both, whichever can give hope to someone suffering silently. A person should not be expected to deal with this by themselves. Although not every person who experiences an injury becomes depressed—just as not every survivor has trouble dealing with their sexuality—the potential of this problem is too real, and the consequences too serious, to be ignored.

I was unable to locate a figure that would tell me how many people commit suicide after surviving a TBI. My mother had a cousin who did this terrible act to himself. I am certain that this number would make medical professionals take notice of a possible epidemic. My children took the dubious privilege of suicide away from me. I couldn't be so selfish as to leave my girls with such a legacy. But without treatment for depression, some people might not make it to the point where life is meaningful enough again for them to value. I may be wrong about the coincidence of suicide and TBI, but just about every person with a brain injury I assisted when I worked for communityworks made mention of having had thoughts of suicide at some time.

The need to address issues of sexuality and depression, and to assess suicidal thoughts or ideation in counseling is a must. They should be a topic of discussion during at least one treatment session each week, especially with a newly disabled person. All of my experiences—surviving a TBI, my lifelong rehabilitation, having to grow up all over again and then becoming a mother of three, nurturing my family, and working in the field of rehabilitation—have made me want to share how vital it is to address the issues of sex, depression, and suicide. My hope is that after exposure to this material, a family member, caregiver, or medical professional in daily contact with a person who is having difficulty accepting their new role, may rethink their attitude about how to counsel, and how to care for, a person who happens to have a "different ability" (instead of a "disability"). Rehabilitation professionals and family members alike need to address these three issues as thoroughly and readily as they address issues related to mobility, self-care, or bowel and bladder management.

I can only hope, that a person trudging up this hill to recovery; somehow, someway, someday, comes across this book and realizes through my example that although a life of rehabilitation is tough, it is all worth it.

A person should never sugarcoat the truth, because let me tell ya, if someone can live through a brain injury, they can see right through the lies. Furthermore, if a person can survive a TBI, they deserve the respect to be spoken to directly about the battle that they are going to fight. Too often conversations about them take place right in front of them, with all of the words seemingly traveling right through them to their loved one's ears as if they weren't even there. Often doctors aren't even aware that they are doing this—speaking through the injured as if they can't understand what they are saying about them, their injury, or their future. Survivors should be involved in their treatment options. They should be a part of evaluating all the choices that affect their lives, given a chance to be part of the decision-making process, and most of all, communicated with *like an adult.*

In treating survivors with as much respect as you would anyone else, whether in the hospital or in their own home, you begin to satisfy the need everyone has to have his opinion be seen as valid and worthwhile. The disempowered patient begins to regain his sense of empowerment.

Today, almost two decades later, I am still coping with the ramifications of the impact I experienced. Areas which weren't so necessary for survival, like the swollen discs in my neck, were ignored so that my strength could be routed to the areas most vital to staying alive. As I persist on my rehabilitation journey my body continues to have to adjust to my uneven gait, to broken bones that healed incorrectly distorting my posture, and to the uneven weight distribution on my skeletal system. It is easy to forget that we are all so fragile. Always remember to buckle in both your children and yourselves.

People who have experienced a trauma need, even more than everyone around them, to realize that life is all about change, and that you keep learning until the day you die. This new life is nothing but change.

Just recently, my sister Debbie told me that signs of the "Old Becky" had started to re-emerge. She said, "Maybe it is not the, 'Old Becky.' It could be that she is like a chrysalis. She has been in a cocoon since the accident. I think that the butterfly from within is getting ready to fly."

Above all, remind survivors of the slim chances that they had to survive, and yet they did. Say to them: "You can't just give into everything. Your life has meaning. Why let these challenges take your life? It hasn't so far, and you're still here today to prove it. Show 'em what you've got and beat the odds. You've done it once, you can do it again!"

~Appendix 1~

My Milestones

The journey back towards independence insists that a TBI survivor achieve certain milestones. The end result is to create a rehabilitated individual able to do many things medical staff may never have thought possible. My milestones took place throughout my journey as I proved my abilities in test after test and, in a sense, became an adult again.

Milestone #1: *Learning how to make wise decisions on my own.* Coming to a place in life where I trust my ability to make my own decisions and not be dependent on someone else to make the decision for me.

Milestone #2: *Life as therapy.*
Mother made the monumental decision to take me into her home instead of placing me in an institution. In doing so, she chose to take the lead in my therapy, becoming what some might consider my case manager. The alternative would have been to have to learn new life skills in an institutional setting and later on to have to figure out how to transfer all of these skills into your home routine.

Milestone #3: *Realizing the losses.*
Not hiding from reality, not acting as if the injuries aren't present in your life. Accepting that there are significant changes and learning how to put the losses in the past

Milestone #4: *Learning the consequences for everyday actions and behavior.* Getting out of your normal routine, doing something unfamiliar and re-learning how to interact with people.

Milestone #5: *Concentrating on personal goals to increase my quality of life.* Most people realize when they have mastered a challenge. But the real challenge is to keep evaluating your goals. Find the goal that you've always wanted to achieve but never thought you would be able to.

Milestone #6: *Accepting my different abilities.*
This milestone is one that you work on your entire life. But don't let that discourage you: take it on, show your self over and over that you can still get things accomplished. It may be a bit slower; you may need to ask for more help than you would have before the sudden reorganization of your brain, but damn it you can still do it!

Milestone #7: *Determination to complete goals.*
I tell myself that therapy is my job, and I won't quit until I am satisfied with the work that I have accomplished!

Milestone #8: *What I can and cannot do.*
Learning not to get stuck on something that is not showing any progress—such as realizing that because of vision difficulties you might never be able to pass the eye exam and safely drive again. In my case, I would work on things that I knew could show improvement and not dwell on the things that I knew couldn't change, like the smoothness or speed of my gait. I knew how much I could do, and that I could walk a bit faster with a cane, so I just walked with the cane until everything began to work more smoothly together.

Milestone #9: *Accepting that the friends I have, the places I go, and the things I do have changed.*

I knew the group of people I had spent my playtime with probably weren't going to be calling me every weekend any more. My weekend life had changed, and people weren't knocking at my door like they once did. Trying not to be angry about their sudden lack of interest, I decided to find something else I liked to do during those hard times. This helped me realize that feeling sorry for myself is a waste of my time and energy. I turned my angry energy into something positive. I found that I could meet people in other places, through school, volunteering, and support groups or church. I began to look on the bright side telling myself, "Well, now that I don't have to go into work everyday, I don't have to wait for the weekends anymore. I can have fun on any day."

Milestone #10: *True friends shine through.*
I could definitely see who the people were that cared about me. They stuck with me through the tough times and weren't embarrassed to be around me. Let me tell you, there was a drastic reduction of friendships, but that's okay, it weeded out all of the bad ones.

Milestone #11: *Concentrate on today and tomorrow.*
It is so easy to get caught up in the, "I would have, or I could have" frame of mind. We have today to use to shape our future. I think it is a waste of time to get caught up in the past. Yesterday is over. There's nothing you can do about it, but change your attitude.

Milestone #12: *Every day is a new day.*
Maybe you had a bad day yesterday. Going over and over it in your mind just increases your feelings of guilt or regret. To get out of this trap, I had to learn to treat each new day as a clean slate. I might make mistakes, but I can learn from them. I can choose new ways of thinking and feeling without being bound by the past.

Questionnaire Requested by Rebekah Vandergriff in Preparation for *What Day Is It?*

What was your initial reaction to hearing news of the accident?

At what point did you realize what was involved in recovery from a coma state?

What was your reaction when you first tried to communicate with Becky?

Did you ever think that a head injury was such a long recovery process?

Did you consider Becky would never be able to walk or talk again?

Can you describe an incident when you thought there would be no future for Becky?

Was humor ever a strategy in helping you deal with your loss of Becky?

Did you realize Becky decided that "Becky" died on 6/03/89 by Traumatic Brain Injury, and "Rebekah" was born once "Becky" realized she would never be the same person she was before?

What was the point when you realized Rebekah could prove that all the doctors were wrong?

Did you ever notice Rebekah was auditory sensitive and easily agitated?

Did you realize the confusion Rebekah experienced in conversations or simple concepts?

Explain the difference you have noticed in "Rebekah" as compared with "Becky"?

Any form of writing is accepted:

Poems

Paragraphs or Memories

Hopes and Dreams of the Rehabilitation Process

A letter to "Becky" and then to "Rebekah"

cc: Carl Bettis, Sam Dyer, Sam Dyer Jr., Sharon Eiker, Tina Maicher, Renée Senten, Deborah Sweeney, Nancy Williams, Katy Wolfe.

~Appendix 3~
Suggested Contacts
&
Internet Resources

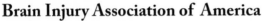

Brain Injury Association of America
1608 Spring Hill Road, Suite 110
Vienna, VA 22182

Phone: (703) 761-0750
Fax: (703) 761-0755
www.biausa.org

National Brain Injury Information Center
(Brain Injury Information Only)
1 (800) 444-6443

www.BrainInjurySuccess.org
A website dedicated to people living with a brain injury and those who care for them.
For more information contact:
GarryandJessica@BrainInjurySuccess.org

Or write:
Garry Prowe & Jessica Whitmore
7025 NW 52nd Drive
Gainesville, FL 32653

Centre for Neuro Skills
1 (800) 922-4994
www.neuroskills.com

communityworks, inc.
7819 Conser Place
Overland Park, KS 66204
(913) 789-9900
www.communityworksinc.com
Service provider for individuals with disabilities, offices in Overland Park, Topeka, and Lawrence, Kansas.

www.disabilityresources.org/SEX.html
(an online directory of websites dealing with sex and disability)

"Disability, Sexuality and Dating" online at
www.disabled-world.com/artman/publish/disabilitysexuality.shtml

Good Days Ahead:
The Interactive Program for Depression and Anxiety
http://mindstreet.com
A multimedia learning program using Cognitive Therapy.

Lash & Associates Publishing/Training Inc.
Brain injury resource, cognitive games, research, personal stories, chat rooms for survivors, caregivers, or families, all materials in DVD, CD, and book formats.

708 Young Forest Drive
Wake Forest, NC 27587-9040
(919) 562-0015
www.lapublishing.com

National Association State Head Injury Administrators
4330 East West Highway, Suite 301
Bethesda, MD 20814

301-656-3500 (Phone)
301-656-3530 (Fax)
Normal business hours: 9 a.m. to 5 p.m. ET, Monday-Friday
www.nashia.org

nashia@nashia.org

Contact us with questions, comments, and suggestions around brain injury-related State systems development.
If you or a family member is in a brain injury-related crisis, call 1-800-444-6443 for confidential resource support.

National Institute of Mental Health
"The largest scientific organization in the world dedicated to research focused on the understanding, treatment, and prevention of mental disorders and the promotion of mental health."
www.nimh.nih.gov

National Spinal Cord Injury Association
1 Church Street #600
Rockville, MD 20850
Toll-Free Helpline: (800) 962-9629
info@spinalcord.org / www.spinalcord.org

www.sexualhealth.com/channel/view/disability-illness
Website for the Sexual Health Network: "dedicated to providing easy access to sexuality information, education, support, and other resources."

Traumatic Brain Injury Survival Guide
(available to read online at **www.tbiguide.com**)
by Dr. Glen Johnson, Clinical Neuropsychologist and Clinical Director of the Neuro-Recovery Head Injury Program
5123 North Royal Drive,
Traverse City, MI 49684
(231) 935-0388
E-mail: debglen@yahoo.com

Suicide Hotline:
1 (800) 333-4444 or 1 (800) SUICIDE

Dept. of Mental Health:
1(800) 634-9687

Rehabilitation Services:
Call 1(800) 432-2326 V/TDD to find an office serving your area.

ALSO SEE YOUR LOCAL YELLOW PAGES UNDER "COUNSELING"

ഇഇരു

Suggestions for Further Reading

Abramson, J.S. "Orienting social work employees in interdisciplinary settings: Shaping professional and organizational perspectives.", *Social Work*, 38, 152-157.

Berger, Robert L., McBreen, James T., & Rifkin, Marilyn J. (1996). *Human Behavior: A Perspective for the Helping Professions*. Longman Publishers USA.

Condeluci, A. (1999, May). "Inclusion: Human Services and Culture." Paper presented at the Brain Injury Association of Florida: *After TBI* in Orlando, Florida.

Condeluci, A., Cooperman, S., & Seif, B.A., (1987). "Independent living: Settings and supports." In M. Ylvisaker, & E. R. Gobble Eds., *Community Re-Entry for Head Injured Adults* (pp. 301-348) . Boston, MA: College-Hill Press.

Delores, M. J., (1997). *Head Injury: Missouri Head Injury Guide for Survivors, Families, and Caregivers*. (5th printing). Columbia, MO: Instructional Materials Laboratory.

Falconer, J., (1998). "Recovering from Head Injury: Managing Behavior Problems." *Journal of Head Trauma Rehabilitation*, 13 (1) 69-79.

Gronwall, D., Wrightson, P., & Waddell, P. (1998). *Head Injury: the facts: a guide for families and care-givers.* Oxford, New York: Oxford University Press Inc.

Jameson, Larry and Beth. (2007) *Brain Injury Survivor's Guide: Welcome to Our World.* Outskirts Press.

Krammer, Peter D. (2005). *Against Depression.* New York, New York: Penguin Group (USA) Inc.

Marett, K., Gibbons, W., Memmott, R., Bott R., & Duke, L. (1998). "The Organizational Role of Clinical Practice Models in Interdisciplinary Collaborative Practice." *Clinical Social Work Journal*, 26, (2), 217-225.

Mitchell, B., & Williams, J., (4) 1-21. IV. "From the Medical Model to Independent Living." Training Material: *Heading Home On The HCBS/HI Waiver.* (1999).

Osborn, Claudia L. (1998) *Over My Head: A Doctor's Own Story of Head Injury from the Inside Looking Out.* Kansas City, Missouri: Andrews McMeel Publishing.

Oxford, M., & McDonald, G., (6) 1-8. "History of Independent Living." Training Material: *Heading Home On The HCBS/HI Waiver.* (1999).

Pipher, Mary Ph.D. (1994). *Reviving Ophelia: Saving the Selves of Adolescent Girls.* New York, New York :The Berkley Publishing Group, Penguin Group (USA) Inc.

Racino, J., & Williams, J. (1994). "Living in the community: An Examination of the Philosophical and Practical Aspects. *Journal of Head Trauma Rehabilitation*, 9, (2), 35-48.

Ratey, John J. (2001). *A User's Guide to the Brain: Perception, Attention, and the Four Theaters of the Brain.* New York, New York: Pantheon Books, a division of Random House, Inc.

Resnick, C., & Tighe, G. (1997). "The role of Multidisciplinary Community Clinics in Managed Care Systems." *Social Work*, 42, (1), 91-98.

Rocchio, Carolyn. (1999). "Can Families Manage Behavioral Programs in Home Settings?" [Brain Injury Source] Orlando, Florida.

Schofield, R., & Amodeo, M. (1999). "Interdisciplinary Teams in Health Care and Human Services Settings: Are They Effective?" *Health and Social Work*, 24, (3), 210-219.

Singer, G., Powers, L.E., & Olson, A.L. (1996). *Redefining Family Support; Innovations in Public-Private Partnerships.* Baltimore: Paul H. Brookes Publishing Co.

Strong, B., & DeVault C. (1994). *Human Sexuality.* Mountain View, CA: Mayfield Publishing Company.

Swiercinsky, Denise P., Price, Terrie L & Leaf, Leif Eric. (1997). *Traumatic Head Injury: Cause, Consequence, and Challenge.* (9th printing). The Brain Injury Assoc. of Kansas & Greater Kansas City, Inc.

Whitehouse, M., & McCabe, M. (1997). "Sex Education Programs for People with Intellectual Disabilities: How Effective Are They?" *Education and Training in Mental Retardation and Developmental Disabilities*, 229-238.

Williams, Janet M. & Kay, Thomas. (1991). *Head injury: A family Matter.* Baltimore, Maryland: Paul H. Brooks Publishing Co.

Williams, J. & Matthews, M. (1998). *Independent Living and Brain Injury: Overview, Obstacles, and Opportunities.* University of Kansas: RTC/IL for Underserved Populations.

Ylvisaker, M., & Feeneey, T. (1994). "Communication and Behavior: Collaboration Between Speech-Language Pathologists and Behavioral Psychologists." *Topics in Language Disorders,* 15, 37-50.

Zasler, N., & Kreutzer, J. (1991). "Family and Sexuality After Traumatic Brain Injury." In *Head Injury: a Family Matter.* Williams & Kay (Eds.), (pp. 253-270). Baltimore, MD: Paul H. Brookes Publishing Co.

CPSIA information can be obtained at www.ICGtesting.com
Printed in the USA
BVOW02s1806151015

422694BV00001B/12/P